IN THE BEGINNING

Chariot Books

from
David C. Cook

IN THE BEGINNING

Published by David C. Cook Publishing Co., Elgin, IL 60120

Printed in the United States of America
Library of Congress Catalog Number: 78-60940
ISBN: 0-89191-157-X

Design by Kurt Dietsch and Larry Taylor

IN THE
BEGINNING

1st DAY

there was darkness—darkness and silence. God created heaven and earth. His Spirit moved through the darkness and across the waters. God said, "Let there be light": and there was light. How beautiful the light was! Then God divided the light from the darkness and called the light Day and the darkness Night.

2nd DAY

God made the sky.
In the sky He placed clouds
to hold the moisture.
And the sky was called Heaven.

3rd DAY Then God gathered
together the waters under the sky. He called
these "seas" and He named the dry land
"earth." On the land He made grass and flowers,
and trees, and in each was the seed to
replenish itself. The fruitful earth was
to become a place of beauty.

4th DAY

To light the earth, God made the sun to shine by day, and the moon to shine by night...The days, the years, and the seasons were also set by God. Then He made the stars and placed them in the heavens.

5th DAY

God looked upon the land and seas and said: "Let the waters bring forth life"—and the seas and rivers became alive with whales and fish...
"Let there be birds"—and the open sky above the earth was filled with winged creatures.
"Be fruitful and multiply," God said as He blessed the living creatures of the sea and sky.

6th DAY

Then God said, "Let the earth bring forth living creatures"... and animals of all kinds filled the earth. So the waters, the sky, and the earth were filled with life. To have dominion over all these things, God created the first man, Adam, and the first woman, Eve. They were the greatest of all God's creations, for He gave them a mind to choose between good and evil, and a soul that would live forever.

And on the seventh day God rested...

God took Adam and Eve to the garden of Eden and showed them the beauty and fruitfulness of it. And God commanded: Of every tree thou mayest eat freely... but of the tree of knowledge of good and evil thou mayest not eat, for in the day that thou eatest of it thou shalt surely die...

Temptation in the Garden

FROM GENESIS 3

LOOK, ADAM, HOW THE LITTLE BIRD COMES WHEN I CALL.

GOD IS GOOD TO US, EVE. HE HAS GIVEN US EVERYTHING.

EVERYTHING — BUT THE FRUIT OF THE TREE OF KNOWLEDGE.

YES, THAT IS FORBIDDEN!

BUT EVE WONDERS — AND ONE DAY SHE GOES ALONE TO THE TREE. AS SHE GAZES AT THE FORBIDDEN FRUIT...

BUT ADAM AND EVE KNOW THEY HAVE DISOBEYED GOD. THEN THEY HEAR HIS VOICE CALLING THEM.

I'M AFRAID!

QUICK—LET'S HIDE!

IN THE STILLNESS OF THE GARDEN THEY HEAR GOD ASK: "HAVE YOU EATEN THE FRUIT THAT I TOLD YOU NOT TO EAT?"

EVE GAVE ME SOME FRUIT—AND I ATE IT.

THE SERPENT TEMPTED ME!

"BECAUSE YOU DISOBEYED ME," GOD SAID, "YOU MUST LEAVE THIS BEAUTIFUL GARDEN AND WORK FOR YOUR LIVING."

LOOK! A FLAMING SWORD GUARDS THE ENTRANCE— WE CAN NEVER GO BACK.

WHERE CAN WE GO? WHAT CAN WE DO?

Jealous Brothers

FROM GENESIS 4:1-8

OUTSIDE THE GARDEN OF EDEN THE LAND IS BARREN, HOT AND DRY. WEARY, ALONE AND FRIGHTENED, ADAM AND EVE SEARCH UNTIL THEY FIND A PLACE TO MAKE A HOME.

REMEMBER HOW BEAUTIFUL EDEN WAS? IF ONLY...

YES, IF ONLY WE HAD OBEYED GOD. WE MUST MAKE CERTAIN THAT WE TEACH OUR CHILDREN SO THAT THEY DON'T MAKE THE MISTAKE WE DID!

SO ADAM TEACHES THEIR SONS, CAIN AND ABEL, ABOUT GOD.

HE MADE THE EARTH AND EVERYTHING WE HAVE.

I LIKE TO THINK OF GOD GIVING ME MY LITTLE LAMB.

12

The Verdict
FROM GENESIS 4: 8-26; 5; 6:1-8

IN A LONELY PASTURE, CAIN KILLED HIS BROTHER, ABEL. CAIN IS SURE NOBODY SAW THE MURDER. BUT SUDDENLY THE KILLER IS AFRAID. DID SOMEONE SEE HIM? WHO?

HE LOOKS AROUND... AND THEN HE HEARS THE VOICE OF GOD ASKING: "WHERE IS ABEL, YOUR BROTHER?"

I—I DON'T KNOW. AM I MY BROTHER'S KEEPER?

GOD KNOWS I HAVE KILLED ABEL!

TERRIFIED, CAIN HEARS GOD'S VERDICT—AS PUNISHMENT FOR MURDERING ABEL, CAIN MUST LEAVE HOME AND FOREVER BE A FUGITIVE.

OH, GOD! PLEASE! THIS PUNISHMENT IS MORE THAN I CAN TAKE!

BUT GOD'S SENTENCE WAS CARRIED OUT. CAIN FLED TO A LAND CALLED NOD. THERE HE MARRIED AND BUILT THE FIRST CITY, WHICH HE NAMED FOR HIS SON, ENOCH.

ADAM AND EVE ARE HEARTBROKEN BY THE LOSS OF THEIR TWO SONS.

OUR HOUSE IS SO EMPTY AND STILL. OH, ADAM, WILL WE ALWAYS BE ALONE LIKE THIS?

WE BROUGHT THIS TRAGEDY ON OURSELVES, EVE—AND SO DID CAIN. BUT GOD HAS BEEN GOOD TO US. LET'S ASK HIM TO HELP US NOW...

IN TIME, A THIRD SON IS BORN TO THEM.

WE'LL CALL HIM SETH.

AND WE'LL TEACH HIM TO OBEY GOD THE WAY ABEL DID.

AGAIN ADAM AND EVE'S PRAYERS ARE ANSWERED, FOR SETH LEARNS TO OBEY GOD. TWO OF HIS DESCENDANTS ARE ENOCH WHO "WALKED WITH GOD" AND METHUSELAH WHO DIED AT THE AGE OF 969—THE OLDEST MAN WHO EVER LIVED.

When the Rains Came
FROM GENESIS 6:7-22; 7:1-10

YOUR WICKEDNESS CANNOT CONTINUE! TURN AWAY FROM YOUR IDOL WORSHIP! RETURN TO GOD WHO CREATED US AND GAVE US ALL THAT WE HAVE!

LISTEN TO NOAH! HE THINKS HE'S BETTER THAN ANYONE ELSE!

WHAT'S HIS GOODNESS DONE FOR HIM?

BUT NOAH REMAINS TRUE TO GOD. AND ONE DAY GOD SPEAKS TO HIM: *"THE EARTH IS FILLED WITH VIOLENCE...I WILL DESTROY MAN WHOM I HAVE CREATED. MAKE THEE AN ARK, FOR BEHOLD I WILL BRING A FLOOD OF WATERS UPON THE EARTH."*

NOAH OBEYS—AND SETS TO WORK BUILDING AN ARK ACCORDING TO THE DIRECTIONS GIVEN HIM BY GOD.

POOR NOAH, HE THINKS HE CAN FLOAT A BOAT ON DRY LAND.

WHAT WILL HE THINK OF NEXT?

16

WHEN THE ARK IS COMPLETED, GOD DIRECTS NOAH AND HIS FAMILY TO ENTER... AND TO TAKE WITH THEM SEVEN PAIRS OF EACH KIND OF ANIMAL AND BIRD THAT IS GOOD TO EAT, AND ONE PAIR OF EACH KIND NOT USED FOR FOOD.

The Great Flood

FROM GENESIS 7: 16-24; 8; 9; 11

WATER FLOWS OVER THE LAND AND RISES ABOVE THE MOUNTAIN-TOPS. ALL THE EARTH IS COVERED... ONLY NOAH'S GREAT ARK SURVIVES. THE FLOOD DESTROYS ALL THAT IS EVIL.

AT LAST THE WATER LEVEL DROPS AND THE ARK RESTS ON THE TOP OF THE MOUNTAINS OF ARARAT.

I WILL SEND OUT A DOVE; IF IT DOES NOT COME BACK WE WILL KNOW IT HAS FOUND LAND.

BUT THE DOVE RETURNS!

NOAH SENDS OUT A DOVE AGAIN, AND IT RETURNS.

AN OLIVE BRANCH! THAT MEANS SOME LAND MUST BE DRY AGAIN.

SEVEN DAYS LATER, NOAH SENDS OUT A DOVE A THIRD TIME. IT DOES NOT RETURN BECAUSE IT HAS FOUND A PLACE TO NEST.

SO, A LITTLE OVER A YEAR AFTER THE FLOOD BEGAN, NOAH STEPS ON DRY LAND ONCE MORE. HE, HIS FAMILY AND THE ANIMALS IN THE ARK ARE THE ONLY CREATURES ON EARTH.

HOW GOOD IT IS TO WALK ON THE GROUND AGAIN!

YES—TO FEEL GRASS UNDER YOUR FEET AND WARM SUNSHINE ON YOUR FACE.

ALL THAT WAS EVIL HAS BEEN DESTROYED. THROUGH US, GOD IS GIVING MANKIND A NEW START. WE MUST OBEY GOD—AND TEACH ALL WHO FOLLOW US TO DO SO.

AS SOON AS NOAH LEAVES THE ARK, HE BUILDS AN ALTAR. HERE HE THANKS GOD FOR HIS CARE AND ASKS GOD'S GUIDANCE IN HELPING NOAH AND HIS FAMILY TO MAKE A NEW START. THEN GOD MAKES A PROMISE TO NOAH AND TO ALL HIS CHILDREN, FOREVER...

The Tower that Crumbled

FROM GENESIS 11

A TOWER THAT WILL REACH TO HEAVEN—HOW BEAUTIFUL IT IS!

IT CAN BE SEEN FOR MILES. IN TIME OF DANGER WE WILL RALLY OUR FORCES AROUND IT. NO ONE IS GOING TO CONQUER AND SCATTER US! WITH THIS TOWER, WE'LL BE INVINCIBLE!

BUT GOD IS DISPLEASED WITH THE PEOPLE'S DESIRE FOR FAME AND POWER. TO STOP THEIR WORK ON THE TOWER, HE CAUSES THE PEOPLE TO SPEAK IN DIFFERENT LANGUAGES.

WHAT KIND OF TALK IS THAT? HOW CAN I WORK WITH A MAN I CAN'T UNDERSTAND?

BECAUSE THEY CANNOT UNDERSTAND ONE ANOTHER, THE BUILDERS ARE CONFUSED. THEY STOP WORKING ON THE TOWER. ONE BY ONE, THE FAMILIES WHO SPEAK THE SAME LANGUAGE MOVE AWAY. THE GIANT TOWER, CALLED BABEL, BEGINS TO CRUMBLE...

SOME OF THE FAMILIES MOVE DOWN THE EUPHRATES RIVER —AND THERE BUILD THE GREAT TRADING CITY OF UR. OTHERS PITCH THEIR TENTS ON THE PLAINS BEYOND. THE BIBLE TRACES THE GENERATIONS FROM NOAH'S SON, SHEM, TO A TRIBAL CHIEFTAIN NAMED TERAH WHO LIVES OUTSIDE UR.

ONE DAY IN TERAH'S CAMP THERE IS GREAT EXCITEMENT—EVERYONE IS GETTING READY FOR A TRIP TO UR.

MAY WE TRADE OUR WOOL FOR ANYTHING WE WANT, FATHER?

YES, ABRAHAM. BUT FIRST YOU MUST HELP ME LOAD OUR SUPPLIES.

LOOK! GREEN BEANS AND MELONS!

WE'LL TRADE SOME OF OUR SUPPLIES FOR FRESH VEGETABLES. THEN YOU, HARAN AND NAHOR MAY GO INTO THE CITY.

A THROW STICK FOR YOUR BAG OF WOOL.

IT'S A DEAL!

IMAGINE THROWING A STICK THAT WILL COME BACK TO YOU.

WHAT IS THAT TOWER?

IT IS A TEMPLE TO THE MOON-GOD.

BACK HOME, ABRAHAM THINKS OFTEN ABOUT HIS VISIT TO UR. AND AS HE GROWS OLDER HE WONDERS ABOUT THE TEMPLE OF THE MOON-GOD.

ONE EVENING ABRAHAM TALKS TO SARAH, THE MOST BEAUTIFUL GIRL IN HIS FATHER'S CAMP.

IT'S ONLY THE MOON, SARAH, NOT SOMETHING TO WORSHIP.

ABRAHAM—BE CAREFUL. MANY PEOPLE HERE WORSHIP THE MOON-GOD. THEY MIGHT HEAR YOU AND DO YOU HARM.

WOULD YOU CARE, SARAH?

YES, ABRAHAM. EVERYONE EXPECTS YOU TO BE HEAD OF OUR TRIBE, SOMEDAY.

SARAH, I LOVE YOU AND WANT YOU TO BE MY WIFE. BUT IT'S ONLY FAIR THAT YOU SHOULD KNOW I DO NOT BELIEVE IN THE MOON-GOD. THERE IS ONLY ONE GOD—THE GOD WHO MADE THE MOON, THE STARS, THE SUN— EVEN US!

I LOVE YOU, ABRAHAM. BUT GIVE ME TIME TO THINK...

26

Night Attack

FROM GENESIS 11

27

AT LAST THE GREAT DAY ARRIVES. THE FLOCKS... DONKEYS LADEN WITH SUPPLIES...THE FAMILIES...ALL FORM A GREAT CARAVAN THAT PUSHES NORTH ALONG THE EUPHRATES RIVER.

I WONDER WHAT LIES AHEAD, ABRAHAM.

HAVE NO FEAR, SARAH, GOD WILL GUIDE US.

ASSYRIA

HARAN

MEDITERRANEAN SEA

TIGRIS RIVER

EUPHRATES RIVER

DAMASCUS   NORTH

ARABIAN DESERT

UR

MAP OF TERAH'S JOURNEY.

PERSIAN GULF

AFTER A FEW DAYS OUT ABRAHAM CALLS A MEETING OF NAHOR AND LOT.

IT WILL BE COOLER FOR THE FLOCKS IF WE REST BY DAY AND TRAVEL AT NIGHT.

BUT WHAT ABOUT WILD ANIMALS?

WE'LL HAVE TO BE ON CONSTANT GUARD, NAHOR.

I AGREE WITH UNCLE ABRAHAM.

Into the Unknown
FROM GENESIS 11

I'LL PAY 700 PIECES OF SILVER FOR YOUR CAMELS.

SOLD. HERE, SCRIBE, FIX UP A BILL OF SALE!

ABRAHAM WEIGHS OUT THE SILVER. SOON HE IS RAISING HIS OWN HERDS AND FLOCKS.

ALL GOES WELL IN TERAH'S CAMP UNTIL ONE DAY WORD SPREADS THROUGHOUT THE TENTS—TERAH IS ILL!

THIS IS THE TIME TO TELL YOUR FATHER ABOUT ABRAHAM'S GOD —BEFORE ABRAHAM BECOMES CHIEF!

NO, MY FATHER IS TOO ILL.

THAT NIGHT TERAH, THE OLD CHIEFTAIN, DIES. GRIEF-STRICKEN, HIS SONS LEAVE THE TENT OF THEIR FATHER...

OH, ABRAHAM!

32

A Tight Spot
FROM GENESIS 12: 1-15

MILE AFTER MILE ABRAHAM'S GREAT CARAVAN TRAVELS ON—STOPPING AT WATER HOLES TO REST AND WATER THE FLOCKS.

I KEEP WONDERING— WHAT IF WE'RE ATTACKED, OR THE PASTURES DRY UP, OR...

WE'RE NOT COWARDS, MAN! THERE ARE DANGERS, SURE, BUT ABRAHAM, OUR LEADER, HAS FAITH IN GOD. I'M LEARNING TO HAVE FAITH, TOO!

AT LAST THE CARAVAN REACHES CANAAN. THE PEOPLE THERE ARE FRIENDLY...

SO THE WEARY TRAVELERS MAKE CAMP ON A HIGH HILL. ABRAHAM BUILDS AN ALTAR AND GIVES THANKS TO GOD.

WHEN THE WEATHER GROWS HOT, THE HERDSMEN TAKE THE SHEEP INTO THE COOL VALLEYS.

A LION! HELP!

THE SAVAGE LION ATTACKS—BUT ABRAHAM'S MEN FIGHT BRAVELY.

WE'VE GOT HIM. TAKE CARE OF THE SHEEP!

THE HUNGRY LIONS RETURN DAY AFTER DAY. FINALLY LOT GOES TO ABRAHAM.

WE'LL MOVE SOUTH TO EGYPT UNTIL THE DRY SPELL IS OVER.

THE PASTURES ARE DRY AND WILD ANIMALS ARE ATTACKING THE SHEEP. WHAT CAN WE DO?

SO ONCE AGAIN THE TENTS ARE TAKEN DOWN, CLOTHING PACKED AND THE ANIMALS ROUNDED UP FOR THE MOVE SOUTH.

ABRAHAM, YOU ARE WORRIED. IS SOMETHING WRONG?

YES, SARAH, I'M AFRAID YOU ARE SO BEAUTIFUL THAT SOME MAN IN EGYPT MAY KILL ME SO HE CAN MARRY YOU. WHEN WE REACH EGYPT WE MUST NOT LET THE PEOPLE KNOW YOU ARE MY WIFE.

KILL YOU! OH, ABRAHAM, I'LL DO ANYTHING YOU ASK!

IN EGYPT WHILE ABRAHAM AND LOT INQUIRE ABOUT PASTURE LAND...

WHAT A BEAUTIFUL WOMAN!

WHO ARE YOU?

I'M ABRAHAM'S SISTER.

TAKE HER TO PHARAOH —HE WILL REWARD YOU FOR BRINGING SUCH A BEAUTIFUL WOMAN TO HIS COURT.

PHARAOH'S COURT! WILL I NEVER SEE ABRAHAM AGAIN?

Raiders of Sodom

FROM GENESIS 12: 16-20; 13; 14: 1-13

IN THE EGYPTIAN PALACE, SARAH IS INTRODUCED AS ABRAHAM'S SISTER. PHARAOH IS AMAZED BY HER BEAUTY.

GIVE HER BROTHER, ABRAHAM, GIFTS OF SHEEP, OXEN, CAMELS AND SERVANTS. TRULY, HIS SISTER IS A BEAUTIFUL WOMAN!

OH, ABRAHAM, IF I DID NOT LOVE YOU SO MUCH I COULD NOT LIVE THIS LIE!

BUT SARAH'S PRESENCE IN PHARAOH'S COURT BRINGS TROUBLE. A PLAGUE BREAKS OUT...

THIS SICKNESS CAME UPON US AT THE TIME THE FOREIGN WOMAN WAS BROUGHT HERE. I HAVE LEARNED SHE IS REALLY ABRAHAM'S WIFE—NOT HIS SISTER. GET RID OF HER!

WHEN PHARAOH LEARNS THE TRUTH ABOUT SARAH, HE CALLS FOR HIS SOLDIERS.

BRING ABRAHAM AND SARAH TO ME—NOW!

ABRAHAM! WHY DIDN'T YOU TELL ME THE TRUTH ABOUT YOUR WIFE? TAKE HER—AND GO YOUR WAY—AT ONCE!

PHARAOH'S ORDERS ARE CARRIED OUT AT ONCE, AND ABRAHAM LEAVES EGYPT.

OH, SARAH, FORGIVE ME. ALL THIS LONG JOURNEY FROM UR I TRUSTED GOD, AND HE PROTECTED US. WHEN I BECAME AFRAID AND DID NOT SEEK GOD'S HELP, I WAS A COWARD.

I FORGIVE YOU, ABRAHAM, AND I'M SURE GOD FORGIVES YOU, TOO. SEE, GOD HAS PROTECTED US EVEN WHEN WE FORGOT TO TRUST HIM.

ABRAHAM AND LOT PROSPER—THEIR FLOCKS INCREASE, BUT THEIR HERDSMEN BEGIN TO QUARREL.

ON THE LONG WAY BACK TO CANAAN, ABRAHAM HAS TIME TO THINK ABOUT GOD'S GUIDANCE...AND THE GREAT TRIBAL CHIEFTAIN RETURNS WITH RENEWED FAITH TO THE LAND GOD PROMISED HIM.

MAKE WAY FOR LOT'S SHEEP!

NO! ABRAHAM IS THE CHIEF—HIS FLOCKS COME FIRST!

37

38

A Stranger's Prophecy

FROM GENESIS 16; 17; 18; 19:1-10

"LOOK TOWARD HEAVEN, AND COUNT THE STARS, IF THOU BE ABLE TO NUMBER THEM:...SO SHALL THE NUMBER OF THY DESCENDANTS BE."

LATER, WHEN SARAH COMES TO HIM WITH A PLAN, HE LISTENS...

BY THE CUSTOM OF OUR PEOPLE I CAN GIVE YOU HAGAR, MY HANDMAID, AS A WIFE THAT SHE MIGHT HAVE A SON FOR ME.

GOD HAS PROMISED ME AN HEIR—PERHAPS THIS IS RIGHT...

HAGAR HAS A SON, AND HE IS THE PRIDE OF ABRAHAM'S HEART.

MY ISHMAEL IS A PROUD AND DARING ONE!

REMEMBER, HAGAR, HE IS **MY** SON! I ADOPTED HIM!

AS ISHMAEL GROWS TO BOYHOOD, HE IS THE CENTER OF ATTENTION THROUGHOUT THE CAMP...

...AND THE SOURCE OF TROUBLE BETWEEN HAGAR AND SARAH.

SOME DAY MY SON WILL RULE THIS WHOLE TRIBE!

HAGAR GETS MORE SURE OF HERSELF EVERY DAY!

ABRAHAM WORRIES ABOUT THE TROUBLE IN HIS CAMP. ONE DAY WHILE HE IS RESTING AT NOON TIME AND THINKING ABOUT ISHMAEL, HAGAR AND SARAH, HE LOOKS UP...

THREE STRANGERS APPROACH HIS CAMP. ABRAHAM GREETS THEM AND INVITES THEM TO REST AND EAT WITH HIM.

WHILE THEY ARE EATING, ONE OF THE STRANGERS GIVES ABRAHAM SURPRISING NEWS!

YOUR WIFE, SARAH, WILL HAVE A SON.

WHO ARE THESE STRANGERS TO BRING FALSE HOPE TO ABRAHAM? I AM TOO OLD TO HAVE CHILDREN!

BUT SARAH IS NOT THE ONLY ONE WHO OVERHEARS THE NEWS. HAGAR ALSO LISTENS AND IS AFRAID...

IF SARAH HAS A SON, WHAT WILL HAPPEN TO ISHMAEL —AND ME!

WHEN THE STRANGERS LEAVE, ABRAHAM WALKS A WAY WITH THEM.

THAT CITY OF SODOM IS SO WICKED THAT GOD MAY HAVE TO DESTROY IT.

THIS IS A MESSENGER FROM GOD! THEY ARE TALKING ABOUT THE PLACE LOT LIVES!

ABRAHAM PRAYS FOR SODOM, AND GOD PROMISES THAT THE CITY WILL BE SAVED IF THERE ARE TEN GOOD MEN IN IT.

Lost in the Desert

FROM GENESIS 19:11-30; 21:1-16

OUTSIDE LOT'S HOUSE IN SODOM, THE MOB GOES WILD. RIOTERS HOWL FOR REVENGE AGAINST LOT AND THE STRANGERS WHO RESCUED HIM.

COME ON— WE'LL BREAK DOWN THE DOOR!

AS THE MEN PUSH AGAINST LOT'S DOOR, THE ANGELS STRIKE THE RIOTERS BLIND.

HELP! I CAN'T SEE!

MY EYES— WHO HIT ME?

INSIDE LOT'S HOUSE...

RUN FOR YOUR LIVES! THE LORD HAS SENT US TO DESTROY THIS WICKED CITY!

MY FAMILY— I MUST SAVE THEM!

BUT LOT'S SONS-IN-LAW ONLY LAUGH WHEN HE TRIES TO WARN THEM. THEY REFUSE TO LEAVE THE DOOMED CITY, SO, EARLY THE NEXT MORNING, THE TWO ANGELS LEAD LOT, HIS WIFE AND THEIR TWO DAUGHTERS AWAY. SUDDENLY ALL SODOM BURSTS INTO FLAME!

LOT'S WIFE STOPS...LOOKS BACK LONGINGLY...AND IS TURNED INTO A PILLAR OF SALT...SO ONLY LOT AND HIS TWO DAUGHTERS ESCAPE GOD'S PUNISHMENT.

DON'T LOOK BACK AT THE CITY—OR YOU WILL ALSO DIE!

I DON'T CARE WHAT GOD SAYS—I WANT TO GO BACK!

NEXT MORNING, ABRAHAM GOES TO THE HILLTOP TO WORSHIP—AND SEES THE SMOULDERING RUINS OF THE WICKED CITY...

AS SURELY AS NIGHT FOLLOWS DAY, DESTRUCTION FOLLOWS SIN. O GOD, HELP ME TO LEAD MY PEOPLE IN THE PATHS OF RIGHTEOUSNESS!

EAGER TO LEAVE THE RUINS OF SODOM, ABRAHAM MOVES TO BEER-SHEBA, NEAR THE DESERT. HERE, SARAH'S SON IS BORN.

ABRAHAM HAS NAMED HIS SECOND SON, ISAAC.

WHAT WILL BECOME OF ISHMAEL, HIS FIRST SON? HE MIGHT HAVE BEEN OUR RULER AFTER ABRAHAM, BUT NOW THE BABY, ISAAC, WILL RULE OUR PEOPLE.

I'M AFRAID THERE WILL BE TROUBLE.

SARAH AND HAGAR BECOME MORE JEALOUS DAY BY DAY. THEN AT THE BABY ISAAC'S FIRST FEAST...

SEE HOW CLUMSY LITTLE ISAAC IS!

ISHMAEL! BE QUIET!

SARAH IS ANGRY! WHAT WILL SHE DO?

HAGAR'S SON CAN'T MAKE FUN OF MINE! ABRAHAM, YOU MUST SEND ISHMAEL AND HAGAR AWAY, BEFORE THEY CAUSE TROUBLE IN THE TRIBE.

NIGHT AFTER NIGHT, ABRAHAM SEEKS GOD'S ANSWER TO HIS PROBLEM. FINALLY, HE KNOWS WHAT HE MUST DO.

46

Test of Faith

FROM GENESIS 21:17-21; 22:1-10

DEAD TIRED AND CHOKING WITH THIRST, HAGAR TURNS HER BACK ON HER SON, ISHMAEL... SHE CANNOT WATCH HIM DYING. SUDDENLY SHE HEARS A VOICE. IT'S GOD SAYING: "LIFT UP THE LAD, FOR I WILL MAKE HIM A GREAT NATION".

HAGAR STARTS TOWARD HER SON ... AND SEES A SPRING NEARBY.

WATER! WE WILL NOT DIE! O ISHMAEL, GOD HAS SAVED US!

DRINK, MY SON, GOD IS WITH US. WE NEED NEVER BE AFRAID AGAIN!

KNOWING GOD IS WITH THEM, HAGAR AND ISHMAEL CONTINUE THEIR JOURNEY TO A PLACE IN THE WILDERNESS WHERE THEY BUILD A HOME. YEARS PASS—ISHMAEL MARRIES AN EGYPTIAN GIRL AND BECOMES THE HEAD OF A GREAT DESERT TRIBE.

IN ABRAHAM'S CAMP, THE YEARS PASS SWIFTLY, TOO. YOUNG ISAAC PROVES HIMSELF A WORTHY SON OF THE TRIBE'S GREAT LEADER.

HE STOLE MY STAFF!

IF YOU TOOK HIS STAFF, RETURN IT. AND YOU, EBER, REMEMBER THAT WE DON'T SETTLE QUARRELS WITH OUR FISTS.

ISAAC WILL MAKE A GOOD LEADER FOR OUR TRIBE.

YES, BUT WHY IS ABRAHAM TAKING THE BOY ON THIS SUDDEN JOURNEY? ABRAHAM ACTS AS IF HE DOESN'T WANT TO GO...

ABRAHAM IS STUNNED... FOR AS A TEST OF FAITH, GOD HAS TOLD HIM TO SACRIFICE HIS SON.

THE WHOLE CAMP WONDERS AS ABRAHAM AND ISAAC SET OUT...

AND AS THEY NEAR A MOUNTAINTOP, ISAAC'S CURIOSITY GROWS...

SOMETHING'S WRONG! I'VE NEVER SEEN MY FATHER AFRAID... BUT HE IS NOW.

50

Secret Mission to Haran

FROM GENESIS 22: 11-18;
23: 1, 2, 19, 20; 24: 1-10

WITH JOYOUS HEARTS, ABRAHAM AND ISAAC GIVE THANKS TO GOD. AND ABRAHAM HEARS GOD'S PROMISE: "THROUGH YOU, ALL NATIONS OF THE EARTH SHALL BE BLESSED."

ON THE WAY HOME, ISAAC WALKS AHEAD—AND ALONE. THROUGH HIS MIND FLASH SCENES OF THE DAY. HE CAN STILL FEEL THE ROPES THAT TIED HIM ON THE ALTAR...SEE HIS FATHER'S DAGGER...FEEL THE JOY OF KNOWING HE WOULD NOT BE KILLED.

SARAH RUSHES OUT OF THE CAMP TO GREET THEM.

ISAAC, MY SON, WHAT HAPPENED? YOU LEFT HERE A BOY—YOU HAVE RETURNED A MAN—LIKE YOUR FATHER, STRONG, TALL, WISE.

FROM MY FATHER I LEARNED THE COST OF FAITH... AND FROM GOD, THE REWARD.

IN THE YEARS THAT FOLLOW, THE TRIBE OF ABRAHAM PROSPERS. THEN ONE DAY, SAD NEWS SPREADS THROUGHOUT THE CAMP...SARAH IS VERY SICK.

A Bride for Isaac

FROM GENESIS 24:11-67; 25:7, 8

ABRAHAM'S SERVANT REACHES HARAN IN THE EVENING. HE RESTS BY THE TOWN'S WELL AND SEES YOUNG WOMEN OF THE CITY COMING TO GET WATER.

O GOD, GIVE ME A SIGN! LET THE ONE WHO GIVES WATER TO ME AND MY CAMELS BE ISAAC'S BRIDE!

HOW BEAUTIFUL SHE IS! WILL SHE BE THE ONE?

PLEASE GIVE ME A DRINK.

I'LL BE GLAD TO—AND I'LL DRAW WATER FOR YOUR CAMELS, TOO.

SHE IS THE ONE!

WHEN THE GIRL HAS FINISHED WATERING THE CAMELS, THE SERVANT GIVES HER EARRINGS AND GOLD BRACELETS.

WHAT IS YOUR NAME? DO YOU THINK THERE IS ROOM FOR ME TO STAY IN YOUR FATHER'S HOUSE?

HOW BEAUTIFUL THESE PRESENTS ARE! MY NAME IS REBEKAH, AND WE HAVE ROOM FOR YOU IN OUR HOUSE. WAIT...

REBEKAH RUNS TO TELL HER FAMILY. WHEN SHE SHOWS THE PRESENTS, LABAN, HER BROTHER, GOES OUT TO MEET ABRAHAM'S SERVANT.

COME! MY FATHER HAS ROOM FOR YOU AND YOUR CARAVAN.

ABRAHAM'S SERVANT TELLS WHO HE IS AND EXPLAINS THAT GOD HAS CHOSEN REBEKAH TO BE THE BRIDE OF ISAAC, SON AND HEIR OF ABRAHAM, HER GREAT UNCLE.

TAKE REBEKAH TO BE THE WIFE OF MY UNCLE'S SON— AS THE LORD HAS SPOKEN.

EARLY THE NEXT MORNING, THE CARAVAN GETS READY TO RETURN TO ABRAHAM'S CAMP. REBEKAH SAYS GOOD-BY TO HER FAMILY AND THE CARAVAN BEGINS ITS LONG JOURNEY.

The Scheming Brother

FROM GENESIS 25: 9-33

THE WHOLE TRIBE MOURNS THE DEATH OF ITS GREAT LEADER, ABRAHAM. THROUGHOUT THE CAMP THERE IS A STIR OF UNEASINESS. BEHIND ISAAC'S BACK MEN WHISPER, "WILL ISHMAEL COME?" ONE DAY, A GREAT CLOUD OF DUST RISES IN THE DISTANCE...

IT'S ISHMAEL! WITH A BAND OF RIDERS!

BREATHLESSLY, THE WHOLE CAMP LOOKS ON AS ISAAC GOES OUT TO MEET HIS BROTHER.

ISHMAEL— MY BROTHER!

THAT SAME DAY THE TRIBE OF ABRAHAM JOURNEYS TO THE BURIAL CAVE OF MACHPELAH—TO PLACE THE BODY OF ITS GREAT CHIEFTAIN BESIDE HIS WIFE, SARAH. BUT IN THE MIDST OF THEIR GRIEF, THE PEOPLE ANXIOUSLY WATCH ISHMAEL...

BUT ISHMAEL, LIKE ISAAC, HAS KNOWN THE LOVING CARE OF GOD. THE OLDER BROTHER HAS NO THOUGHTS OF REVENGE.

IS IT WELL WITH YOU AND YOUR PEOPLE, ISHMAEL?

I HAVE TWELVE SONS. MY TRIBE IS POWERFUL. THE SONS OF ABRAHAM WILL LIVE IN PEACE, MY BROTHER.

TIME AND AGAIN GOD HAD TESTED ABRAHAM'S FAITH... AND BY FAITH ABRAHAM HAD OBEYED. TIME AND AGAIN, TOO, GOD HAD PROMISED TO MAKE ABRAHAM THE FOUNDER OF GREAT NATIONS...AND THROUGH HIS SONS THE PROMISE WAS FULFILLED.

UNDER ISAAC'S PEACEFUL LEADERSHIP, THE TRIBE CONTINUES TO GROW. THE PEOPLE ARE LOYAL, EVEN WHEN ISAAC MOVES THEM FROM PLACE TO PLACE TO AVOID WAR WITH NEIGHBORING TRIBES OVER WATER HOLES THAT ARE RIGHTFULLY HIS. BUT ISAAC FAILS TO SEE THE CONFLICT BETWEEN HIS OWN SONS.

WHICH ONE WILL RULE OUR TRIBE AFTER ISAAC?

ESAU—IT IS HIS BIRTHRIGHT BECAUSE HE WAS BORN FIRST.

WHEN ESAU RETURNS WITH FOOD, ISAAC PRAISES HIM.

ESAU IS A MIGHTY HUNTER.

MY TIME WILL COME —AND SOON!

JACOB BIDES HIS TIME... ONE MORNING, DURING A HOT SPELL, ESAU SETS OUT FOR A HUNTING TRIP... THIS IS THE CHANCE JACOB HAS BEEN WAITING FOR.

GAME WILL BE AT THE WATER HOLE, MILES AWAY. HE'LL BE TIRED AND HUNGRY AFTER THE LONG DAY'S HUNT. I'LL BE READY FOR HIM.

TOWARD SUNDOWN JACOB WAITS FOR HIS BROTHER OUTSIDE CAMP.

HERE HE COMES— AND WITHOUT ANY GAME!

CAMP WITH ITS FOOD IS ONLY A SHORT DISTANCE AWAY, BUT ESAU IS SO HUNGRY HE CANNOT WAIT...

I'M STARVED... GIVE ME SOME OF THE STEW.

WILL YOU TRADE YOUR BIRTHRIGHT FOR IT?

Cry of Revenge

FROM GENESIS 25: 32-34; 27: 1-41

ISAAC HAS GROWN OLD. HIS EYESIGHT IS FAILING. NOW HE DECIDES IT IS TIME TO GIVE HIS ELDEST SON THE BLESSING WHICH WILL INCLUDE RULING THE TRIBE.

YOU CALLED ME, FATHER?

YES, ESAU. I AM OLD AND TIRED—AND I DON'T KNOW HOW SOON I SHALL DIE. BRING ME SOME CHOICE VENISON AND I WILL GIVE YOU THE BLESSING THAT SEALS YOUR BIRTHRIGHT.

THE NEWS REBEKAH OVERHEARS SENDS HER RUNNING THROUGH THE CAMP...

FIND JACOB! TELL HIM TO COME TO HIS MOTHER'S TENT— AT ONCE! HURRY!

LISTEN, JACOB! YOUR FATHER IS GETTING READY TO GIVE ESAU THE BLESSING. YOU MUST GET THAT BLESSING, OR THE BIRTHRIGHT YOU GOT FROM ESAU MEANS NOTHING.

BUT WHAT CAN I DO?

BEFORE YOU AND YOUR BROTHER WERE BORN, THE LORD SPOKE TO ME AND SAID: "THE ELDER SHALL SERVE THE YOUNGER." BUT ESAU WILL SERVE YOU ONLY IF YOU ARE CHIEF OF THE TRIBE.

MY SKIN IS SMOOTH, BUT ESAU IS HAIRY. FATHER WILL TOUCH ME AND KNOW I AM NOT ESAU. WHAT CAN WE DO?

I HAVE THOUGHT OF THAT, TOO. HERE, PUT ON ESAU'S ROBE—THESE SKINS ON YOUR ARMS AND NECK WILL MAKE YOU FEEL LIKE ESAU.

BUT WHAT IF...

GOD GIVE THEE OF THE FATNESS OF THE EARTH...LET PEOPLE SERVE THEE...AND NATIONS BOW DOWN TO THEE...BE LORD OVER THY BRETHREN...CURSED BE EVERY ONE THAT CURSETH THEE, AND BLESSED BE HE THAT BLESSETH THEE.

NO SOONER IS THE BLESSING GIVEN, THAN JACOB RUSHES OUT OF HIS FATHER'S TENT.

MOTHER! THE BLESSING IS MINE! BUT WHAT WILL ESAU SAY?

NO MATTER WHAT ESAU SAYS, THE BLESSING IS YOURS. NOT EVEN YOUR FATHER CAN TAKE IT BACK NOW!

BUT WHILE JACOB AND HIS MOTHER ARE REJOICING, ESAU RETURNS.

Tricked

FROM GENESIS 27:42-46; 28; 29:1-25

WITH ESAU'S THREAT TO KILL JACOB RINGING IN HER EARS, THE SERVANT GIRL RUNS TO REBEKAH'S TENT.

ESAU IS GOING TO KILL JACOB!

ESAU IS UPSET—TELL NO ONE WHAT YOU HAVE HEARD. FIND JACOB AND TELL HIM TO COME TO ME— AT ONCE!

YOU MUST GO AWAY UNTIL YOUR BROTHER'S ANGER COOLS. GO TO MY BROTHER, LABAN, IN HARAN. I WILL SEND FOR YOU WHEN IT IS SAFE TO RETURN.

WHAT WILL I TELL MY FATHER?

ONCE AGAIN, REBEKAH PAVES THE WAY FOR HER FAVORITE SON.

ISAAC, ESAU'S WIVES ARE A GREAT TROUBLE TO ME. LIFE WILL NOT BE WORTH LIVING FOR ME IF JACOB MARRIES A WOMAN OF THIS COUNTRY. IF ONLY HE COULD MARRY A GIRL FROM MY PEOPLE—REMEMBER HOW YOUR FATHER'S SERVANT FOUND ME AT MY FATHER'S HOUSE IN HARAN AND BROUGHT ME TO YOU?

ISAAC'S THOUGHTS GO BACK OVER THE YEARS TO THE DAY HE FIRST SAW REBEKAH. HE ALSO KNOWS THERE WILL BE TROUBLE BETWEEN HIS SONS. HE SENDS FOR JACOB.

ASHAMED, BUT FRIGHTENED BY ESAU'S ANGER, JACOB COMES TO HIS FATHER.

GO TO THY MOTHER'S BROTHER, LABAN, AND FIND A WIFE FROM AMONG HIS FAMILY. GOD BLESS YOU, MY SON.

A FEW HOURS LATER—AT THE EDGE OF CAMP...

GOOD-BY, MY SON. I'LL SEND WORD WHEN IT IS SAFE TO RETURN.

MY FATHER IS OLD—I MAY NEVER SEE HIM AGAIN. ESAU WANTS TO KILL ME. OH, MOTHER, YOU ARE THE ONLY ONE I WILL BE ABLE TO COME BACK TO!

ONE PUNISHMENT FOR THEIR DECEIT IS THAT REBEKAH AND JACOB NEVER SEE EACH OTHER AGAIN.

TRAVELING FARTHER AND FARTHER FROM HIS FAMILY AND FRIENDS, JACOB IS TORTURED BY LONELINESS. HE ESPECIALLY MISSES HIS MOTHER, WHO HAS ALWAYS PROTECTED AND ADVISED HIM. HE IS HAUNTED BY THE MEMORY OF HOW HE TRICKED HIS FATHER AND BROTHER.

AS NIGHT APPROACHES...

IT'S GETTING DARK...I'LL HAVE TO STOP HERE TONIGHT.

JACOB SOON FALLS ASLEEP... AND HE DREAMS OF A SHINING LADDER, REACHING UP TO HEAVEN. ON THE LADDER ARE ANGELS, GOING UP AND DOWN AS IF BRINGING HELP FROM GOD. AND JACOB HEARS GOD SPEAK TO HIM, PROMISING TO TAKE CARE OF HIM AND BRING HIM SAFELY HOME AGAIN.

THE NEXT MORNING JACOB AWAKENS, STILL AWED BY THE DREAM HE HAD.

SURELY GOD IS IN THIS PLACE—AND THIS IS THE GATE OF HEAVEN.

JACOB REALIZES THE WRONG HE HAS DONE. BUT HE KNOWS THAT GOD WILL HELP HIM IF HE OBEYS HIM. QUICKLY HE TURNS A STONE ON END FOR AN ALTAR AND WORSHIPS GOD. HE CALLS THE PLACE BETH-EL, WHICH MEANS "THE HOUSE OF GOD."

IF GOD WILL GO WITH ME, I'LL BE GOD'S MAN.

JACOB GOES ON HIS WAY A STRONGER, NOBLER YOUNG MAN BECAUSE HE HAS FOUND GOD. HE IS EAGER TO PUT BEHIND HIM THE DISHONESTY OF HIS PAST AND BECOME REALLY WORTHY OF GOD'S LOVE AND CARE.

SHEPHERDS AROUND A WELL. MAYBE THEY CAN HELP ME FIND MY UNCLE LABAN.

CAN YOU DIRECT ME TO THE CHIEFTAIN, LABAN?

LABAN? WHY, YES. THAT FLOCK OF SHEEP IS HIS. THAT'S HIS DAUGHTER, RACHEL, WITH THEM!

WHAT A BEAUTIFUL GIRL!

QUICKLY HE ROLLS THE STONE FROM THE WELL AND HELPS RACHEL WATER THE SHEEP. WHEN HE TELLS WHO HE IS, SHE RUNS TO TELL HER FATHER.

THAT NIGHT, LABAN HOLDS A FEAST FOR HIS NEPHEW, JACOB. LEAH, THE ELDER DAUGHTER, SERVES THE FOOD, WHILE RACHEL LISTENS TO JACOB AS HE TELLS OF HIS HOME AND LONG JOURNEY TO HARAN.

Bargain in the Desert

FROM GENESIS 29:26—32:6

SO JACOB MARRIES RACHEL AND BEGINS HIS SECOND SEVEN YEARS OF WORK FOR LABAN. UNDER JACOB'S CARE THE FLOCKS CONTINUE TO INCREASE. AT THE END OF THE SEVEN YEARS JACOB THREATENS TO LEAVE, BUT LABAN MAKES ANOTHER BARGAIN: JACOB CAN HAVE ALL OF THE SPECKLED OR SPOTTED ANIMALS. SO, JACOB STAYS; AND IN A FEW YEARS HIS FLOCKS OUTNUMBER LABAN'S. LABAN BECOMES ANGRY...

ONE DAY JACOB CALLS HIS WIVES TO HIM.

I CAN SEE THAT TROUBLE IS RISING IN THE TRIBE. IT IS BETTER IF WE LEAVE WHILE YOUR FATHER IS AWAY. HELP ME PACK, AND WE WILL GO AT ONCE.

THE CAMEL TRAIN IS QUICKLY PACKED, THE FLOCKS HERDED TOGETHER; SOON THE CARAVAN IS ON ITS WAY.

LABAN MAY FOLLOW— KEEP WATCH AND TELL ME IF YOU SEE HIM COMING.

AS THEY TRAVEL, JACOB GUARDS THE CAMEL ON WHICH HIS BELOVED RACHEL AND HER ONLY SON, JOSEPH, ARE RIDING. LEAH AND JACOB'S OTHER TEN SONS WATCH WITH JEALOUS EYES. WITHOUT REALIZING IT, JACOB IS SOWING SEEDS OF TROUBLE FOR THE SON HE LOVES THE BEST...

SEVERAL DAYS AFTER LEAVING LABAN...

LOOK—RIDERS! LABAN AND HIS MEN. QUICK—TELL JACOB!

JACOB IS READY WHEN HIS FATHER-IN-LAW ARRIVES.

JACOB, WHY DID YOU LEAVE WITHOUT GIVING ME A CHANCE TO SAY GOOD-BY?

I WAS AFRAID YOU MIGHT HAVE KEPT YOUR DAUGHTERS FROM GOING.

I HAVE ENOUGH MEN SO I COULD TAKE REVENGE ON YOU. BUT THE GOD OF YOUR FATHERS HAS TOLD ME NOT TO HARM YOU.

SO LABAN AND JACOB SET UP A HEAP OF STONES AS A MARKER AND MAKE AN AGREEMENT NEVER TO HARM EACH OTHER.

THE LORD WATCH BETWEEN ME AND THEE, WHEN WE ARE ABSENT ONE FROM ANOTHER.

THE NEXT MORNING LABAN RIDES AWAY.

73

EAGERLY JACOB CONTINUES HIS JOURNEY HOME. ON THE WAY HE HAS A WONDERFUL VISION...

AN ARMY OF ANGELS! THE HOSTS OF GOD ARE CAMPED BESIDE ME!

HE IS COMFORTED BY THE ANGELS—BUT AS HE NEARS HIS HOME COUNTRY, HE BEGINS TO WORRY ABOUT HIS BROTHER, ESAU, WHO ONCE PLANNED TO MURDER HIM.

RIDE AHEAD—SEARCH OUT ESAU. TELL HIM I AM RETURNING HOME WITH MY FAMILY AND FLOCKS. TELL HIM I HOPE HE WILL FORGIVE ME.

JACOB WAITS ANXIOUSLY FOR THE RIDERS TO COME BACK. HE REMEMBERS THE TIME WHEN HE LIED TO HIS FATHER AND STOLE HIS BROTHER'S BLESSING...WHEN ESAU THREATENED TO KILL HIM...

FINALLY THE SCOUTS RETURN...

WE SAW ESAU! HE'S COMING TO MEET YOU— WITH 400 MEN!

Journey to Hebron

FROM GENESIS 32:7—33; 35:1-20

JACOB IS FRIGHTENED...
BUT HE IS ALSO SHREWD. HE DIVIDES HIS CARAVAN
INTO TWO SECTIONS, AND SENDS SERVANTS AHEAD
WITH PRESENTS FOR ESAU.

IF ESAU ATTACKS ONE GROUP, THE OTHER CAN ESCAPE.

THAT NIGHT JACOB PRAYS—CONFESSING HIS SINS, ADMITTING HIS FEAR, AND ASKING GOD'S HELP. BUT STILL HE CANNOT SLEEP.

MY FAMILY WOULD BE SAFER ON THE OTHER SIDE OF THE RIVER.

SO, IN THE MIDDLE OF THE NIGHT, HE MOVES HIS FAMILY...

YOU WILL BE SAFER ON THE OTHER SIDE, RACHEL.

I WISH YOU WOULD STAY WITH US.

BUT JACOB NEEDS TO BE ALONE... AND LATER THAT NIGHT AS HE PRAYS, HE FEELS HIMSELF WRESTLING WITH A MYSTERIOUS STRANGER. IT IS A FIERCE STRUGGLE, BUT JACOB DOES NOT GIVE UP UNTIL THE STRANGER BLESSES HIM: "THY NAME SHALL BE CALLED NO MORE JACOB, BUT ISRAEL: FOR AS A PRINCE HAST THOU POWER WITH GOD."

THE NEXT MORNING JACOB FINDS HIMSELF LAME FROM WRESTLING WITH THE ANGEL. BUT JACOB IS HAPPY...FOR HE KNOWS HIS EVIL NATURE HAS BEEN CONQUERED AND THAT HE HAS BEEN BLESSED BY GOD. JACOB GOES CONFIDENTLY TO MEET HIS BROTHER.

JACOB, MY BROTHER! I AM HAPPY TO SEE YOU AGAIN!

ESAU! HOW GLAD I AM. YOU DO NOT HATE ME ANY MORE!

PROUDLY JACOB PRESENTS HIS FAMILY...

AND THIS IS MY WIFE, RACHEL, AND MY SON, JOSEPH.

IT IS GOOD TO SEE MY BROTHER'S FAMILY. GOD HAS BLESSED YOU MUCH.

AFTER FEASTING TOGETHER, THE BROTHERS SAY GOOD-BY. JACOB HEADS TOWARD HIS FATHER'S HOME IN HEBRON.

FAREWELL, AND GREET MY FATHER FOR ME.

I WILL TELL HIM ALL IS WELL WITH YOU. GOOD-BY, AND GOD BLESS YOU, ESAU.

SOME TIME LATER ON THE WAY, JACOB STOPS AT BETH-EL.

THIS STONE, RACHEL, MARKS THE PLACE WHERE I SAW ANGELS COMING TO ME FROM HEAVEN, AND WHERE GOD PROMISED TO TAKE CARE OF ME. HE HAS, RACHEL...MORE THAN I DESERVE.

GOD HAS BEEN GOOD TO US, JACOB. AND I PRAY THAT HE WILL TAKE CARE OF OUR SON, JOSEPH— AND THE CHILD WHO IS SOON TO BE BORN.

FARTHER ALONG ON THE JOURNEY— NOT FAR FROM BETHLEHEM—RACHEL'S CHILD IS BORN...

IT'S A BOY, BUT OH, MY MASTER, YOUR WIFE, RACHEL, IS DEAD !

JACOB BURIES HIS BELOVED WIFE, RACHEL. THEN HE AND HIS FAMILY CONTINUE SADLY ON THEIR JOURNEY...STOPPING NOW AND THEN TO REST AND FEED THE FLOCKS. AS THEY TRAVEL ON, JACOB WONDERS...

RACHEL AND MY MOTHER ARE DEAD. WILL I GET TO MY FATHER WHILE HE IS STILL ALIVE ?

Into the Pit

FROM GENESIS 35: 27-29; 37: 1-26

JACOB'S HAND TREMBLES AS HE SHADES HIS EYES AND LOOKS TOWARD THE DISTANT CITY OF HEBRON.

IS THAT WHERE MY GRANDFATHER, ISAAC, LIVES?

YES, JOSEPH. I PRAY WE ARE NOT TOO LATE... HE IS VERY OLD.

JACOB'S PRAYERS ARE ANSWERED. AT THE SIGHT OF HIS BLIND AND AGED FATHER, HE FALLS TO HIS KNEES.

O FATHER, I AM YOUR SON, JACOB—THANK GOD, I AM WITH YOU AGAIN.

JACOB, MY SON! I HAVE PRAYED FOR YOUR RETURN. DO YOU HAVE CHILDREN NOW?

PROUDLY JACOB PRESENTS HIS 12 SONS TO THEIR GRANDFATHER, ISAAC.

FATHER, THESE ARE JOSEPH AND BENJAMIN, THE SONS OF MY BELOVED RACHEL.

BE STRONG, MY CHILDREN, AND OBEY GOD ALWAYS.

WHEN THE OLDER SONS RETURN, THEY ARE JEALOUS OF JOSEPH'S COAT. THEN HE TELLS THEM ABOUT HIS DREAMS...

LAST NIGHT I DREAMED WE WERE BINDING SHEAVES, AND ALL OF YOUR SHEAVES BOWED DOWN TO MINE.

BOW DOWN TO HIM? **NEVER'!**

STILL LATER JOSEPH HAS ANOTHER DREAM...

I DREAMED THE SUN AND MOON AND STARS BOWED TO ME.

WHAT? SHALL YOUR PARENTS AND BROTHERS SERVE YOU?

JACOB SOON FORGETS HIS OWN ANGER TOWARD JOSEPH, BUT THE SECOND DREAM WHIPS THE OLDER BROTHERS' HATRED INTO A BURNING RAGE.

SEVERAL DAYS LATER THE BROTHERS ARE TENDING THE SHEEP SOME DISTANCE FROM CAMP, AND JACOB SENDS JOSEPH TO SEE HOW THEY ARE GETTING ALONG.

HERE COMES THE DREAMER.

I'VE HAD ENOUGH OF HIS TALK. LET'S GET RID OF HIM!

Slave Train to Egypt

FROM GENESIS 37: 27-36; 39:1-20

BUT JOSEPH'S SUCCESS ALSO LEADS TO TROUBLE. POTIPHAR'S WIFE FALLS IN LOVE WITH THE HANDSOME, YOUNG SLAVE. ONE DAY WHILE POTIPHAR IS AWAY...

JOSEPH, COME, SIT BESIDE ME. TELL ME WHERE YOU CAME FROM AND WHY YOU ARE IN EGYPT.

THANK YOU, BUT I HAVE WORK TO FINISH BEFORE POTIPHAR RETURNS.

MUST YOU ALWAYS THINK OF POTIPHAR?

HE IS MY MASTER— I WILL NOT BE UNTRUE TO HIM OR DISOBEY MY GOD.

NO MAN CAN SCORN ME—AND LIVE!

SHE BIDES HER TIME...WHEN POTIPHAR RETURNS SHE GREETS HIM WITH TEARS IN HER EYES, AND A LIE ON HER LIPS.

YOUR HEBREW SLAVE TRIED TO KISS ME! I SCREAMED AND HE LEFT...BUT HE DROPPED HIS ROBE. HERE— SEE IT!

I'LL THROW HIM IN PRISON FOR THIS!

BEFORE THE SUN SETS THAT DAY, JOSEPH IS CHAINED AND THROWN INTO THE KING'S PRISON.

HO— WHAT A HANDSOME PRISONER WE HAVE WITH US!

WHEN HE'S BEEN HERE AS LONG AS I HAVE, HE'LL FORGET WHAT IT'S LIKE TO WEAR SUCH FINE, CLEAN CLOTHES.

The King's Dream

FROM GENESIS 39: 21-23; 40; 41;
42:1-6

FALSELY ACCUSED, JOSEPH FACES HIS FIRST NIGHT IN PRISON. BUT HE IS NOT AFRAID, AND HE IS NOT ALONE BECAUSE GOD IS WITH HIM. JOSEPH PRAYS... AS HE HAS DONE EVERY OTHER NIGHT IN HIS LIFE.

WHAT GOD CAN SAVE HIM NOW?

LEAVE HIM ALONE! HE IS BRAVER THAN THE REST OF US.

ONE LONG, HOT DAY FOLLOWS ANOTHER. THE PRISONERS QUARREL OVER FOOD—WATER—THE BEST PLACE TO SLEEP. ONE DAY A FIGHT BREAKS OUT...

STOP IT! FIGHTING WON'T HELP US.

EVEN IN PRISON GOD IS WITH JOSEPH. WHEN THE KEEPER OF THE JAIL LEARNS JOSEPH IS A LEADER, HE PUTS JOSEPH IN CHARGE OF THE OTHER PRISONERS.

86

FROM THE THRONE ROOM, JOSEPH GOES TO HIS OWN ROOM AND KNEELS IN PRAYER, THANKING GOD FOR PROTECTION AND GUIDANCE.

JOSEPH ORDERS THE PEOPLE TO START PREPARING FOR THE FAMINE. HE BECOMES FAMOUS, AND ALL REJOICE WHEN HE MARRIES THE BEAUTIFUL DAUGHTER OF THE PRIEST OF ON.

I AM PROUD TO BE YOUR WIFE, JOSEPH. YOU HAVE DONE SO MUCH FOR OUR PEOPLE.

THERE IS MORE TO BE DONE, MY DEAR. THE YEARS OF PLENTY WILL PASS QUICKLY.

ALL TOO SOON, THE FAMINE BEGINS. AS IT CONTINUES, PEOPLE FROM OTHER COUNTRIES COME TO EGYPT SEEKING FOOD. ONE DAY TRIBESMEN FROM CANAAN ENTER JOSEPH'S CITY...

IN ORDER TO BUY GRAIN, THEY APPEAR BEFORE THE GOVERNOR OF EGYPT. THEY BOW BEFORE HIM...

MY BROTHERS! THEY DO NOT RECOGNIZE ME AFTER ALL THESE YEARS!

Trouble in Egypt

FROM GENESIS 42: 6-38

THE TEN SONS OF JACOB STAND BEFORE THE GOVERNOR OF EGYPT—NOT KNOWING THAT HE IS JOSEPH, THE BROTHER THEY SOLD INTO SLAVERY YEARS BEFORE. BUT JOSEPH RECOGNIZES HIS HALF-BROTHERS— AND DECIDES TO FIND OUT WHETHER THEY HAVE LEARNED TO BE KIND AND MERCIFUL.

YOU ARE SPIES!

NO, MY LORD! WE ARE TEN OF THE SONS OF THE GREAT CHIEFTAIN, JACOB. HE SENT US TO BUY GRAIN.

TEN SONS? HOW MANY MORE SONS DOES YOUR FATHER HAVE?

HE HAD TWELVE—THE YOUNGEST, BENJAMIN, IS HOME WITH OUR FATHER. THE OTHER ONE DIED LONG AGO!

I STILL SAY YOU ARE SPIES. GUARDS —TAKE THEM TO PRISON!

WHY SHOULD HE THINK WE'RE SPIES?

I DON'T KNOW—BUT IT WAS STRANGE THAT THE GOVERNOR WANTED TO KNOW HOW MANY SONS OUR FATHER HAD.

ON THE THIRD DAY THE BROTHERS ARE ONCE MORE BROUGHT BEFORE JOSEPH.

YOU MAY BUY GRAIN— BUT TO MAKE SURE YOU ARE NOT SPIES, I WILL HOLD ONE OF YOU IN PRISON UNTIL YOUR YOUNGEST BROTHER IS BROUGHT TO ME.

ME—IN PRISON?

HOURS PASS...THE BROTHERS TRY TO UNDERSTAND WHAT HAS HAPPENED—BUT NEVER ONCE DO THEY SUSPECT THAT THEIR BROTHER JOSEPH IS THE GOVERNOR.

THIS MUST BE PUNISHMENT FOR WHAT WE DID TO JOSEPH LONG AGO.

I TOLD YOU NOT TO HARM HIM!

HAS IT TAKEN YOU ALL THESE YEARS TO REGRET THE EVIL YOU DID THAT DAY?

THE ONE BROTHER SIMEON IS QUICKLY BOUND AND TAKEN TO PRISON AS A HOSTAGE. FRIGHTENED AND EAGER TO LEAVE EGYPT, THE OTHER BROTHERS HURRY TO THE STOREHOUSE FOR GRAIN.

PAY ME FIRST— THEN I'LL FILL YOUR SACKS.

THE GRAIN SACKS FILLED, THE BROTHERS LEAVE EGYPT AT ONCE. THAT NIGHT AS THEY SET UP CAMP...

LOOK! THE MONEY I PAID FOR THE GRAIN!

IT'S A TRAP! I TELL YOU THERE'S SOMETHING MYSTERIOUS ABOUT EVERYTHING THAT'S HAPPENED SINCE WE CAME TO EGYPT!

I'D NEVER GO BACK EXCEPT—

EXCEPT THAT WE LEFT SIMEON THERE IN PRISON. AND BENJAMIN IS THE ONLY ONE WHO CAN SET HIM FREE.

WHO KNOWS— MAYBE NEXT TIME WE COME THE GOVERNOR WILL KEEP BENJAMIN— OR ONE OF US!

FOR DAYS, AS THE CARAVAN TRAVELS NORTHEAST THE BROTHERS WORRY ABOUT WHAT THEIR FATHER WILL SAY.

BACK HOME, THEY PROUDLY SHOW THEIR FATHER HOW MUCH GRAIN THEY HAVE BROUGHT...

LOOK— THE MONEY IS IN MY SACK, TOO!

AND MINE!

WHAT IS THIS? MONEY IN YOUR GRAIN SACKS— AND WHERE IS SIMEON?

IN—IN PRISON IN EGYPT, AND...

91

The Stolen Cup

FROM GENESIS 43:1—44:12

THEY ENTER THE COURTYARD OF THE GOVERNOR... WHO THEY DO NOT KNOW IS THEIR BROTHER JOSEPH.

WE ARE THE SONS OF JACOB COME AGAIN FOR GRAIN. WHEN WE RETURNED HOME FROM BUYING FOOD, WE FOUND MONEY IN OUR SACKS. WE HAVE BROUGHT THAT MONEY WITH US—AND MORE TO BUY MORE GRAIN.

MY MASTER KNOWS YOU HAVE COME. WAIT HERE—

SIMEON!

O BENJAMIN, THANK GOD YOU CAME!

YOU ARE ALL RIGHT?

YES, BUT I WAS AFRAID YOU'D NEVER COME. THE PRISON WAS DARK AND LONELY. ALL I COULD THINK OF WAS THE EVIL I HAD DONE IN MY LIFE.

FORGET THE PAST, SIMEON. WE ARE ELEVEN BROTHERS AND WE WILL STICK TOGETHER.

THEN—TO THEIR SURPRISE—THE BROTHERS ARE LED INTO A GREAT BANQUET HALL. THE GOVERNOR OF EGYPT STANDS WAITING...

BUT EVEN AS THEY WONDER, THE GOVERNOR HAS THE BROTHERS SERVED — GIVING THE LARGEST PORTION TO BENJAMIN. IT IS A SIGN OF GREAT HONOR.

DO YOU SEE THAT?

AT LEAST BENJAMIN IS SAFE!

THE BANQUET ENDS; THE NEXT MORNING THE BROTHERS BUY THEIR GRAIN AND LEAVE. BUT THEY ARE HARDLY OUT OF THE CITY BEFORE A CHARIOT OVERTAKES THEM.

STOP! ONE OF YOU HAS STOLEN MY MASTER'S SILVER CUP!

YOUR MASTER'S CUP? WE ARE INNOCENT! SEARCH US IF YOU WILL.

IF THE CUP IS FOUND, THE MAN IN WHOSE SACK IT IS HIDDEN SHALL BECOME MY MASTER'S SLAVE!

ONE BY ONE THE SACKS ARE SEARCHED... AT LAST THE OFFICER OPENS BENJAMIN'S...

THE CUP!

Joseph's Secret

FROM GENESIS 44:13—45:26

South into Egypt

FROM GENESIS 45:27, 28; 47; 48; 50:1-15

THE EXCITING NEWS SPREADS QUICKLY THROUGHOUT THE CAMP. SOON THE TRIBE OF JACOB BEGINS MOVING SOUTH TOWARD EGYPT. ON THE WAY JACOB STOPS TO WORSHIP AT A PLACE WHERE HE HAD WORSHIPED AS A BOY.

THAT NIGHT GOD SPEAKS TO HIM IN A VISION: "FEAR NOT TO GO DOWN INTO EGYPT, FOR I WILL GO WITH THEE."

DOWN IN EGYPT, JOSEPH AND HIS FAMILY WAIT ANXIOUSLY!

IS MY GRANDFATHER RICH AND POWERFUL LIKE PHARAOH?

NOT LIKE PHARAOH, MY SON, BUT HE IS THE CHIEF OF A TRIBE.

WHEN I WAS JUST A YOUNG BOY HE GAVE ME A BEAUTIFUL COAT OF MANY COLORS.

DO YOU STILL HAVE THE COAT?

IT WAS TAKEN FROM ME BEFORE I CAME TO EGYPT MANY YEARS AGO...

FOR A MOMENT JOSEPH RELIVES THE TIME WHEN HIS BROTHERS SOLD HIM AS A SLAVE. SUDDENLY A MESSENGER INTERRUPTS HIS MEMORIES...

EXCELLENCY, YOUR FATHER AND BROTHERS ARE CAMPED IN GOSHEN!

JOSEPH HURRIES TO HIS CHARIOT AND RACES TOWARD HIS FATHER'S CAMP.

FATHER! O, MY FATHER!

MY SON! GOD HAS ANSWERED MY PRAYERS.

BACK IN THE CITY, JOSEPH PROUDLY PRESENTS HIS FATHER TO PHARAOH, WHO GIVES JACOB THE BEST PASTURE LAND IN ALL EGYPT.

MAY GOD BLESS YOU FOR YOUR KINDNESS TO US.

FOR SEVENTEEN YEARS JACOB AND HIS SONS LIVE HAPPILY IN EGYPT. THEN ONE DAY A MESSENGER BRINGS SAD NEWS TO JOSEPH...

SIR, YOUR FATHER IS VERY ILL. HE WANTS YOU AND YOUR SONS TO COME—RIGHT AWAY!

THEY HURRY TO JACOB'S BEDSIDE.

BRING YOUR SONS TO ME SO I CAN BLESS THEM BEFORE I DIE.

MAY GOD, WHO HAS GUIDED ME ALL MY LIFE, BLESS MY GRANDSONS.

THEN JACOB CALLS ALL OF HIS SONS TO HIM AND BLESSES THEM. JACOB DIES AND HIS SONS CARRY THE OLD CHIEFTAIN'S BODY BACK TO HIS HOMELAND OF CANAAN.

BECAUSE OF THE WICKEDNESS OF HIS OLDER SONS, JACOB GIVES THE FAMILY BIRTHRIGHT TO JOSEPH AND HIS SONS.

AFTER JACOB'S FUNERAL, JOSEPH WALKS AWAY FROM THE CAMP ALONE. HIS BROTHERS WATCH HIM SUSPICIOUSLY...

JOSEPH WAS GOOD TO US WHILE OUR FATHER LIVED, BUT NOW...

HE MAY GET EVEN. THERE'S ONLY ONE THING TO DO...

Death Sentence

**FROM GENESIS 50:15-26;
EXODUS 1:1—2:1, 2**

FOLLOWING THE BURIAL OF THEIR FATHER, JOSEPH AND HIS BROTHERS GO BACK TO EGYPT. BUT THE BROTHERS ARE AFRAID THAT JOSEPH MAY NOW TAKE REVENGE FOR THE EVIL THEY DID TO HIM.

WE HAVE ONLY ONE COURSE TO TAKE— BUT LET'S WAIT UNTIL WE REACH EGYPT.

YES, OUR FAMILIES ARE THERE.

IN EGYPT THE BROTHERS WASTE NO TIME...

TAKE THIS MESSAGE TO OUR BROTHER, JOSEPH.

JOSEPH WEEPS WHEN HE HEARS THE WORDS OF THE MESSENGER.

BRING MY BROTHERS TO ME— IS IT POSSIBLE THAT EVEN YET THEY HAVE NOT LEARNED THAT I HAVE FORGIVEN THEM?

Cry of a Slave

FROM EXODUS 2:3-11

NEXT DAY THE MOTHER SETS ABOUT PREPARING A LITTLE BASKET.

KEEP WATCH, MIRIAM, I'M ALMOST FINISHED.

THEN, CAREFULLY AVOIDING THE EGYPTIAN SOLDIERS, SHE TAKES THE BASKET AND HER TINY SON TO THE RIVER.

BROTHER'S BASKET FLOATS LIKE A LITTLE BOAT!

KEEP WATCH OVER HIM, MIRIAM. OH, MY SON, IT TEARS MY HEART TO SEND YOU AWAY. MAY GOD WATCH OVER YOU AND PROTECT YOU ALWAYS...

MIRIAM HIDES IN THE BULRUSHES AND WATCHES...

THE PRINCESS! WILL SHE SEE THE BABY'S BASKET?

LOOK—WHAT A STRANGE LITTLE BASKET! I WONDER WHAT'S INSIDE IT?

SO THE HEBREW BABY IS RETURNED TO HIS OWN HOME —BUT NOW UNDER THE PROTECTION OF THE KING'S DAUGHTER. THAT NIGHT THE MOTHER, FATHER, MIRIAM AND YOUNG AARON KNEEL AND PRAY...

O GOD, WE THANK THEE FOR SAVING OUR LITTLE SON. HELP US TO TRAIN HIM TO SERVE THEE!

THE LITTLE BOY LIVES IN HIS HOME UNTIL HE IS ABOUT FOUR YEARS OLD. THEN HIS MOTHER TAKES HIM TO THE PALACE TO LIVE WITH THE PRINCESS WHO HAS ADOPTED HIM.

HE WILL BE _MY_ SON. HIS NAME WILL BE MOSES BECAUSE THAT IS LIKE THE WORD THAT MEANS "TO DRAW OUT", AND I DREW HIM OUT OF THE WATER.

YEARS PASS, AND THE BOY MOSES LIVES THE LIFE OF A YOUNG PRINCE IN PHARAOH'S PALACE. HE LEARNS TO WRITE AND READ. LATER HE GOES TO COLLEGE. ONE DAY HE DRIVES THROUGH THE CITY...

...TO A PLACE WHERE HEBREW SLAVES ARE WORKING. AS HE WATCHES THE SLAVES TOIL, HE IS STARTLED BY A MAN'S SCREAM...

The Fiery Bush

FROM EXODUS 2:11—3:4

MOSES JUMPS FROM HIS CHARIOT TO INVESTIGATE...AND FINDS AN EGYPTIAN GUARD BEATING A HEBREW SLAVE.

IN SUDDEN ANGER MOSES STRIKES OUT HARD—

LOOK! HE KILLED THE GUARD!

THE NEXT DAY MOSES RETURNS. WHEN HE SEES TWO HEBREWS FIGHTING, HE TRIES TO STOP THEM.

WHY DO YOU FIGHT AMONG YOURSELVES?

WHO MADE YOU A JUDGE OVER US? ARE YOU GOING TO KILL ME AS YOU DID THAT EGYPTIAN?

IF PHARAOH HEARS OF THIS HE WILL ACCUSE ME OF BEING A TRAITOR. THERE IS ONLY ONE THING FOR ME TO DO, AND I MUST DO IT NOW...

LATER THAT DAY IN THE PALACE...

PRINCE MOSES KILLED AN EGYPTIAN GUARD FOR BEATING A HEBREW SLAVE!

FIND THE TRAITOR—AND KILL HIM!

BUT PHARAOH'S ORDERS ARE TOO LATE...MOSES HAS A HEAD START ON THE SOLDIERS WHO CHASE HIM. HE ESCAPES— AND AFTER LONG, HARD RIDING REACHES THE LAND OF MIDIAN.

MOSES STAYS WEEKS AND THEN MONTHS. HE MARRIES ZIPPORAH AND IN TIME THEY HAVE TWO SONS.

GERSHOM HANDLES HIS SLING VERY WELL.

HE WILL MAKE A GOOD SHEPHERD— LIKE HIS FATHER.

YEAR AFTER YEAR THE FLOCKS OF JETHRO INCREASE. BUT ONE YEAR THE GRASSES DRY UP AND MOSES LEADS HIS SHEEP TO PASTURES NEAR THE MOUNTAIN OF SINAI.

BUT MOSES CANNOT FORGET THE HEBREW PEOPLE IN EGYPT.

I WONDER IF PHARAOH IS STILL ALIVE... AND WHAT HAS BECOME OF MY SISTER MIRIAM AND MY BROTHER AARON?

HE WONDERS, TOO, ABOUT THE HEBREW SLAVES STILL STRUGGLING UNDER THE WHIPS OF EGYPTIAN RULERS. ONE DAY HE LOOKS UP TO SEE A STRANGE SIGHT ON MOUNT SINAI.

A BUSH ON FIRE— YET IT IS NOT DESTROYED!

HE STEPS CLOSER—THEN STOPS. A VOICE FROM THE FIERY BUSH CALLS OUT "MOSES!"

Pharaoh's Revenge

FROM EXODUS 3:4—5:21

HERE AM I!

THE VOICE CONTINUES: "I AM THE GOD OF YOUR FATHERS...GO DOWN TO EGYPT, TELL PHARAOH TO SET THE HEBREWS FREE."

WHO AM I TO SPEAK TO THE PHARAOH OF EGYPT?

MOSES IS AFRAID—AFRAID OF THE PHARAOH OF EGYPT, AFRAID HE CANNOT SPEAK PROPERLY— AFRAID THE HEBREW PEOPLE WILL NOT BELIEVE HIM. BUT GOD ASSURES HIM: "GO— YOUR BROTHER AARON WILL SPEAK FOR YOU. I WILL BE WITH YOU."

ONCE AGAIN MOSES STARTS TOWARD THE BUSH, BUT THE SAME VOICE WARNS HIM: "DO NOT COME NEARER... TAKE OFF YOUR SHOES, FOR THE GROUND ON WHICH YOU STAND IS HOLY GROUND."

MOSES OBEYS. HE RETURNS TO CAMP AND TELLS HIS FATHER-IN-LAW WHAT GOD HAS CALLED HIM TO DO.

GO IN PEACE. GOD WILL STRENGTHEN YOU, AS HE HAS PROMISED.

AND SO MOSES SETS OUT FOR EGYPT WITH HIS WIFE AND SONS.

MEANTIME...IN THE SLAVE HUTS OF EGYPT, THE HEBREWS ARE ASKING GOD TO HELP THEM.

WHILE AARON, THE BROTHER OF MOSES, IS PRAYING, GOD SPEAKS TO HIM: "GO INTO THE WILDERNESS TO MEET YOUR BROTHER."

AARON IS SURPRISED AT THE STRANGE COMMAND. BUT, LIKE MOSES, HE OBEYS. SOON HE IS ALONE IN THE WILDERNESS.

MOSES HAS BEEN GONE FROM EGYPT FOR MANY YEARS. WILL HE KNOW ME? DOES HE KNOW I'M COMING? I WONDER WHAT GOD WANTS US TO DO?

AARON'S QUESTIONS ARE SOON ANSWERED. HE MEETS HIS BROTHER AT MOUNT SINAI.

MOSES! AARON—I HAVE BEEN WATCHING FOR YOU!

HOW DID YOU KNOW I WAS COMING?

GOD TOLD ME YOU WOULD COME —TO HELP ME.

QUICKLY, MOSES EXPLAINS THAT GOD HAS CALLED THEM TO LEAD THE HEBREWS OUT OF SLAVERY IN EGYPT.

Plague of Death

FROM EXODUS 5:22—1:5

WHEN MOSES AND AARON DEMAND THE RELEASE OF THE HEBREW SLAVES, PHARAOH IS FURIOUS—AND MAKES THE SLAVES WORK HARDER THAN BEFORE. IN ANGER THEY TURN AGAINST MOSES. MOSES SEEKS GOD'S HELP AND IS TOLD TO VISIT PHARAOH AGAIN.

SHOW ME HOW POWERFUL YOUR GOD IS.

WHEN THIS ROD STRIKES THE GROUND, IT WILL BECOME A SERPENT.

AARON'S WORDS COME TRUE, BUT PHARAOH ONLY LAUGHS.

YOU ARE CLEVER, BUT MY MAGICIANS CAN DO THE SAME THING.

PHARAOH CALLS FOR HIS OWN MAGICIANS. THEY TOO THROW DOWN THEIR RODS—WHICH BECOME SERPENTS.

SEE?

BUT WHILE PHARAOH WATCHES, THE SERPENT OF AARON DEVOURS THE SERPENTS OF THE EGYPTIAN MAGICIANS. PHARAOH IS STUNNED... BUT HE REFUSES TO ADMIT THAT MOSES' GOD IS MORE POWERFUL THAN THE GODS OF EGYPT.

AGAIN MOSES SEEKS GOD'S HELP... AND AGAIN GOD TELLS HIM WHAT TO DO. IN THE MORNING MOSES AND AARON MEET PHARAOH ON THE BANK OF THE RIVER NILE.

WHAT ARE *YOU* DOING HERE?

BECAUSE YOU WILL NOT LET THE HEBREWS GO, THE RIVER WILL BE TURNED TO BLOOD.

AT MOSES' COMMAND, AARON STRIKES THE WATER WITH HIS ROD AND THE WATER TURNS RED.

I DON'T DARE BATHE IN THAT BLOODY STREAM!

WHEN WOMEN COME TO WASH THEIR CLOTHES IN THE RIVER, THEY ARE TURNED BACK. MEN HAVE TO DIG WELLS TO GET DRINKING WATER. FINALLY THE RIVER IS CLEAR AGAIN, BUT STILL PHARAOH WILL NOT LISTEN TO MOSES' PLEA. AND SO GOD SENDS A DIFFERENT PLAGUE...

IN THE STREETS OF THE CITY...

FROGS—MILLIONS OF THEM... EVERYWHERE!

AND IN THE EGYPTIAN HOMES...

EE-EEK! A FROG IN MY BREAD DOUGH!

EVEN IN THE PALACE...

FROGS IN MY BED! I CAN'T STAND THIS—SEND FOR MOSES AND AARON.

ASK YOUR GOD TO TAKE AWAY THE FROGS, AND I WILL LET THE HEBREWS GO.

IT SHALL BE AS YOU SAY.

BUT WHEN THE FROGS ARE GONE, PHARAOH BREAKS HIS PROMISE. SO STILL ANOTHER PLAGUE DESCENDS ON EGYPT...

FIRST THERE COMES A PLAGUE OF LICE—LATER GREAT SWARMS OF BITING FLIES FILL THE AIR...

ONCE AGAIN PHARAOH PROMISES TO FREE THE HEBREWS. BUT WHEN THE FLIES DISAPPEAR, HE BREAKS HIS WORD. THEN DISEASE BREAKS OUT AMONG THE CATTLE, AND PHARAOH AND HIS PEOPLE SUFFER FROM PAINFUL BOILS.

FATHER, WERE THE SLAVE DRIVERS CRUEL TODAY?

THEY ARE ALWAYS CRUEL, SON, BUT RIGHT NOW THEY ARE SUFFERING FROM TERRIBLE BOILS WHILE WE ARE STRONG AND HEALTHY.

STILL PHARAOH KEEPS THE HEBREWS IN EGYPT. SO A TERRIBLE STORM STRIKES...

HAILSTONES AS BIG AS MY FIST!

THROUGHOUT THE LAND, THE EGYPTIAN FARMERS WATCH THE STORM WITH TERROR.

OUR CROPS ARE RUINED...

...BUT NO HAIL FALLS ON THE LAND WHERE THE HEBREWS LIVE.

LATER, MILLIONS OF LOCUSTS SWARM THROUGH THE LAND. AFTER A STRONG WIND BLOWS THEM AWAY, THE DAY BECOMES AS DARK AS NIGHT.

IT'S SO DARK—I'M AFRAID.

WILL THESE TERRIBLE TROUBLES NEVER CEASE?

Trapped

FROM EXODUS 11:6—14:12

MOSES HAS TOLD THE PEOPLE THAT AT A CERTAIN HOUR DEATH WOULD STRIKE THE FIRST-BORN IN ALL EGYPT. BUT HE HAS ALSO TOLD THEM HOW TO PROTECT THEIR FAMILIES...

NINE TIMES PHARAOH HAS BROKEN HIS PROMISE TO LET US GO— WHAT WILL HE DO THIS TIME?

SURELY THIS WILL BRING OUR RELEASE FROM SLAVERY.

WHY ARE YOU PUTTING LAMB'S BLOOD ON OUR DOOR-POSTS?

GOD TOLD MOSES IT WOULD BE A SIGN FOR THE ANGEL OF DEATH TO PASS OVER OUR HOUSE.

THAT EVENING, EVERY HEBREW FAMILY GETS READY TO LEAVE EGYPT. THEY EAT A FEAST CALLED THE PASSOVER BECAUSE THE ANGEL OF DEATH WAS PASSING OVER THEIR HOMES.

THE NEXT DAY THE GREAT EXODUS FROM EGYPT IS ON ITS WAY. JOYFULLY THE HEBREWS MARCH TOWARD THE LAND GOD HAS PROMISED THEM WILL BE THEIR HOME. THEY ARE GUIDED BY A BRIGHT CLOUD BY DAY...

AND A PILLAR OF FIRE BY NIGHT.

BUT IN THEIR RUSH FOR FREEDOM THEY DO NOT FORGET TO TAKE WITH THEM THE BODY OF THEIR GREAT LEADER, JOSEPH.

HE WAS A GREAT MAN IN EGYPT, BUT HE ASKED TO BE BURIED IN HIS HOMELAND.

AFTER SEVERAL DAYS OF TRAVEL, THEY REACH THE RED SEA...

THE SEA IS IN FRONT OF US AND THE MOUNTAINS ALL AROUND.

WHAT WILL WE DO NOW? WHERE CAN WE GO?

Crossing the Sea

FROM EXODUS 14:10—16:10

PHARAOH AND HIS ARMY LOOK AT THE HEBREWS CAMPED BESIDE THE RED SEA.

TRAPPED—JUST AS I SAID!

GOOD! THEY'LL SOON SEE WHO IS MIGHTIER—PHARAOH OR THE GOD THEY WORSHIP!

AT THE SAME TIME IN THE HEBREW CAMP...

I'D RATHER SERVE THE EGYPTIANS THAN DIE THIS WAY!

FEAR NOT, STAND STILL, AND SEE THE SALVATION OF THE LORD. THE EGYPTIANS WHOM YOU SEE TODAY, YOU SHALL SEE NO MORE.

AS MOSES SPEAKS THE CLOUD THAT LEADS THEM MOVES TO THE BACK OF THE CAMP.

LOOK! THE CLOUD IS HIDING US FROM THE EGYPTIANS!

THEN MOSES HOLDS OUT HIS HAND, AS GOD HAD TOLD HIM. A STRONG EAST WIND BLOWS ALL NIGHT AND ROLLS BACK THE WATERS OF THE SEA...

AWED BY THE SIGHT, THE HEBREWS RUSH JOYFULLY ACROSS THE PATH IN THE SEA.

PHARAOH CHARGES, BUT THE HEBREW CAMP IS EMPTY! THE EGYPTIANS RACE OUT ACROSS THE SEA FLOOR, BUT SAND CLOGS THEIR CHARIOT WHEELS...

IN TERROR THEY TRY TO TURN BACK... BUT THE WIND DIES, AND THE WATERS RETURN. ALL OF PHARAOH'S MEN ARE CAUGHT IN THE RUSHING SEA.

SAFE ON THE OTHER SIDE, THE HEBREWS LOOK BACK...

GOD HAS SAVED US!

I'LL NEVER AGAIN DOUBT THAT MOSES WAS SENT BY GOD TO SAVE US FROM THE EGYPTIANS.

JOYFULLY THE HEBREWS CELEBRATE GOD'S DELIVERANCE. THE TRIBES DESCENDED FROM JACOB (ISRAEL) ARE A FREE PEOPLE—READY TO FORM A NEW NATION. MIRIAM, MOSES' SISTER, LEADS THE WOMEN'S CHORUS SINGING PRAISES TO GOD.

THE LORD IS MY STRENGTH AND SONG: HE IS MY SALVATION.

SING TO THE ♪ LORD. ♫

FROM THE RED SEA, THE ISRAELITES MARCH ACROSS THE DESERT. BUT AFTER DAYS OF TRAVEL THEY FORGET WHAT GOD HAS DONE FOR THEM. AND THEY BEGIN TO COMPLAIN...

I'M THIRSTY.

THREE DAYS AND NO WATER IN SIGHT.

AT LAST THEY FIND A SPRING, BUT...

IT'S BITTER! WE CAN'T DRINK THIS!

WE'LL ALL DIE OF THIRST!

MOSES PRAYS TO GOD FOR HELP—AND GOD POINTS OUT A TREE. MOSES THROWS IT INTO THE SPRING.

NOW TASTE THE WATER AND KNOW THE POWER OF GOD!

IT'S PURE NOW.

...GOD HAS SAVED US AGAIN. NOW I _KNOW_ THAT GOD IS GUIDING MOSES!

WITH RENEWED FAITH, THE PEOPLE CONTINUE THEIR JOURNEY. AS THEY TRAVEL ACROSS THE HOT SANDS THEIR THOUGHTS ARE OF THE HOMELAND GOD HAS PROMISED THEM. THEY DREAM OF GREEN FIELDS...FRESH STREAMS...GREAT FLOCKS.

BUT THERE IS NO FOOD IN THE DESERT. THE PEOPLE GROW HUNGRY...THEY FORGET THAT GOD CARED FOR THEM WHEN THEY WERE THIRSTY...ANGRILY THEY GO TO MOSES AND AARON...

LOOK—OUR FOOD IS GONE. HOW CAN WE FEED OUR CHILDREN?

HAVE YOU BROUGHT US OUT HERE IN THE WILDERNESS TO STARVE US TO DEATH?

BY EVENING YOU WILL KNOW WHO BROUGHT YOU HERE!

Attacked!

FROM EXODUS 16:11—17

THAT EVENING GREAT FLOCKS OF QUAIL DROP INTO THE CAMP.

BIRDS! THOUSANDS OF THEM!

FOOD— ENOUGH FOR EVERYONE!

MOSES WAS RIGHT. GOD SENT THE QUAIL TO FEED US. GOD IS LEADING US!

YES—ONLY GOD COULD SAVE US FROM STARVING. NEVER AGAIN WILL I DOUBT GOD'S POWER AND GUIDANCE.

EARLY THE NEXT MORNING THE PEOPLE ARE SURPRISED TO FIND A STRANGE WHITISH COVERING ON THE GROUND.

WHAT IS IT? IT LOOKS LIKE FROST!

IT IS MANNA—FOOD THAT GOD HAS SENT YOU.

HOW GOOD GOD IS TO US—

GATHER WHAT YOU NEED FOR THIS DAY ONLY.

HOW CAN I BE SURE THERE WILL BE MORE TOMORROW? I'D BETTER COLLECT ALL I CAN!

SEE—I'LL PUT THIS EXTRA ASIDE FOR TOMORROW. NO MATTER WHAT HAPPENS TO THE OTHERS, WE WILL NOT GO HUNGRY.

The Mountain Trembles

FROM EXODUS 17:12—19:20

136

THEN MOSES BUILDS AN ALTAR AND LEADS HIS PEOPLE IN A PRAYER OF THANKSGIVING TO GOD.

FRESH FROM THEIR FIRST MILITARY VICTORY, THE ISRAELITES EAGERLY PUSH ON.

ONLY A FEW WEEKS AGO WE WERE SLAVES IN EGYPT. NOW WE ARE FREE MEN— STRONG ENOUGH TO DEFEND OURSELVES!

WHEN WE GET TO THE PROMISED LAND— WE'LL BUILD A NATION—MIGHTIER THAN ALL EGYPT!

WHEN THEY REACH THE WILDERNESS OF MOUNT SINAI, MOSES SETS UP CAMP. ONE DAY A MESSENGER BRINGS HIM GOOD NEWS...

YOUR FATHER-IN-LAW, JETHRO, YOUR WIFE AND SONS ARE ON THEIR WAY TO SEE YOU.

PROUDLY, MOSES SHOWS JETHRO AROUND THE CAMP. AS THE DAYS GO BY, JETHRO MAKES SOME KEEN OBSERVATIONS...

THIS IS WRONG. I MUST SPEAK TO MOSES AT ONCE.

MOSES GOES OUT AT ONCE TO MEET THEM...

HOW GLAD I AM TO SEE YOU!

I HAVE BEEN HEARING THE WONDERFUL THINGS GOD HAS DONE FOR YOU AND YOUR PEOPLE.

137

138

Commandments of God

FROM EXODUS 20—32:19

WHILE THE PEOPLE OF ISRAEL STAND BEFORE MOUNT SINAI, GOD SPEAKS FROM THE MOUNTAIN AND GIVES THEM THE TEN COMMANDMENTS:

I AM THE LORD THY GOD...THOU SHALT HAVE NO OTHER GODS BEFORE ME.

THOU SHALT NOT MAKE UNTO THEE ANY GRAVEN IMAGE.

THOU SHALT NOT TAKE THE NAME OF THE LORD THY GOD IN VAIN.

REMEMBER THE SABBATH DAY, TO KEEP IT HOLY.

HONOUR THY FATHER AND THY MOTHER.

THOU SHALT NOT KILL.

THOU SHALT NOT COMMIT ADULTERY.

THOU SHALT NOT STEAL.

THOU SHALT NOT BEAR FALSE WITNESS...

THOU SHALT NOT COVET...ANYTHING THAT IS THY NEIGHBOUR'S.

GOD GIVES MOSES MORE LAWS, AND WHEN THESE ARE WRITTEN DOWN, MOSES BUILDS AN ALTAR. HE AND HIS PEOPLE MAKE AN AGREEMENT, OR COVENANT, WITH GOD. "ALL THAT THE LORD HATH SAID WILL WE DO," THE PEOPLE PROMISE.

LATER, GOD CALLS MOSES TO COME AGAIN TO MOUNT SINAI. JOSHUA GOES PART WAY WITH HIM. DAYS PASS, AND MOSES DOES NOT RETURN.

WHEN IS MOSES COMING BACK?

CAN WE GO LOOK FOR HIM?

WE DON'T KNOW—BUT YOU MUST NOT FOLLOW HIM UP THE MOUNTAIN. HE IS ALONE WITH GOD.

WHO KNOWS—MAYBE MOSES ISN'T COMING BACK...

IF HE DOESN'T, WHAT WILL WE DO?

LET'S ASK AARON TO MAKE US A STATUE THAT WE CAN WORSHIP.

YES— WE WANT A GOD WE CAN SEE.

FEELING LOST WITHOUT THEIR LEADER, THE PEOPLE FORGET GOD'S COMMANDMENTS AND THEIR PROMISE TO WORSHIP HIM ONLY. THEY BRING THEIR JEWELRY TO AARON WHO MELTS IT AND MAKES A GOLDEN STATUE OF A CALF.

Death to an Idol

FROM EXODUS 32: 20—40: 17

SHOCKED BY THE SIGHT OF MOSES BREAKING THE STONE TABLETS, THE PEOPLE STOP WORSHIPING THE GOLDEN CALF.

WHAT WILL MOSES DO TO US?

AARON, WHERE DID YOU GET THIS IDOL?

THE PEOPLE GAVE ME THEIR GOLD! I THREW IT INTO A FIRE, AND OUT CAME THIS GOLDEN CALF.

THROW IT BACK INTO THE FIRE!

144

145

The Tabernacle

FROM EXODUS 40: 18-38; LEVITICUS 1—10: 2

AFTER MANY WEEKS OF CAREFUL, LOVING WORK THE HOUSE OF GOD, THE TABERNACLE, IS READY...JOYOUSLY THE PEOPLE WATCH AS MOSES CARRIES THE SACRED ARK CONTAINING THE TEN COMMANDMENTS INTO THE TABERNACLE. HE PLACES IT IN A SPECIAL ROOM CALLED THE HOLY OF HOLIES. THEN A CLOUD COVERS THE TABERNACLE AND THE GLORY OF THE LORD FILLS IT.

NOW THE ISRAELITES ARE NO LONGER A MOB OF FLEEING SLAVES. IN THE ONE YEAR SINCE THEY LEFT EGYPT, THEY HAVE BECOME A NATION WITH LAWS, JUDGES AND A PLACE OF WORSHIP.

Fire in Camp

FROM NUMBERS 10—11: 2

EXCITEMENT SPREADS THROUGH THE CAMP AS THE PEOPLE TALK MORE AND MORE ABOUT THE PROMISED LAND TO WHICH GOD IS LEADING THEM. ONE DAY THE BLAST OF TWO GREAT SILVER TRUMPETS FILLS THE AIR...

THAT IS A SIGNAL FOR ALL OF THE PEOPLE TO COME TO THE TABERNACLE. SOMETHING IMPORTANT MUST BE HAPPENING.

THE PEOPLE DROP WHAT THEY ARE DOING, AND HURRY TO THE TABERNACLE.

DOES THIS MEAN WE ARE GOING TO MOVE?

I DON'T KNOW. WE'LL HAVE TO WAIT AND SEE. OUR ORDERS COME FROM GOD.

WHEN EVERYONE HAS GATHERED...

LOOK! THE CLOUD IS LIFTING!

THE SIGN HAS BEEN GIVEN! EAGERLY THE PEOPLE LINE UP FOR THE MARCH TOWARD THE PROMISED LAND! LEADING THEM IS THE SACRED ARK, CARRIED BY THE PRIESTS.

HIGH ON A HILLTOP, MOSES WATCHES AS THE MARCH GETS UNDER WAY.

GOD IS LEADING US, SO WE HAVE NOTHING TO FEAR.

MOSES IS RIGHT—THEY HAVE NOTHING TO FEAR. AND EVEN THOUGH THEY MARCH THROUGH A WILDERNESS, GOD CONTINUES TO PROVIDE MANNA FOR THEM TO EAT.

...BUT AFTER SEVERAL DAYS, THE PEOPLE BEGIN TO COMPLAIN AGAIN...

HOW LONG HAVE WE BEEN EATING THIS STUFF?

I'M GETTING TIRED OF IT.

DON'T WE HAVE ANYTHING ELSE TO EAT?

NO! I KEEP THINKING ABOUT THE MELONS AND MEAT WE HAD IN EGYPT. HOW GOOD THEY WOULD TASTE!

A Family Divided

FROM NUMBERS 11: 2—12: 10

WHEN FIRE BREAKS OUT IN THE ISRAELITE CAMP, THE PEOPLE QUICKLY FORGET THEIR COMPLAINT ABOUT FOOD AND TRY TO BEAT BACK THE FLAMES.

DID GOD SEND THE LIGHTNING TO BURN OUR TENTS?

MAYBE IT'S A WARNING FOR US TO STOP OUR GRUMBLING ABOUT THE FOOD HE HAS GIVEN US.

HELP US, MOSES! THE WHOLE CAMP WILL BE LOST!

ONLY GOD CAN HELP YOU NOW. I'LL PRAY FOR YOU.

AND AS MOSES PRAYS, THE FIRE GOES OUT.

AS THE QUAIL LAND ON THE DESERT, THE
ISRAELITES PICK UP ALL THEY CAN CARRY.

MEAT! ALL
WE CAN EAT!

LET'S STORE UP ALL
WE CAN TO EAT
LATER ON.

HOW MANY
MORE BASKETS
DO I HAVE TO
GATHER?

GET AS MANY AS
YOU CAN. AT LEAST
WE'LL HAVE ALL
WE NEED.

THE PEOPLE STUFF THEMSELVES
UNTIL MANY ARE SICK.

IT SERVES ME
RIGHT. I WAS
TOO GREEDY.

SOON AFTER
THIS, THE
ORDER IS
GIVEN TO
CONTINUE THE
JOURNEY.
ONCE AGAIN,
A CLOUD BY
DAY AND A
PILLAR OF FIRE
BY NIGHT
LEAD THE
PEOPLE...TO
A CAMP SITE
CLOSER TO
THEIR
PROMISED
HOMELAND.

NO SOONER IS CAMP SET UP THAN
MOSES' OWN BROTHER AND SISTER
TURN AGAINST HIM.

MOSES ACTS AS
IF HE IS THE ONLY
SPOKESMAN FOR
GOD. HE SEEMS TO
FORGET, AARON, THAT
YOU ARE THE
HIGH PRIEST.

YOU'RE RIGHT, MIRIAM. IT'S TIME WE HAVE A TALK WITH OUR BROTHER.

IN ANGER, THEY GO TO MOSES...

WE'RE TIRED OF HAVING YOU RUN EVERYTHING, MOSES. DO YOU THINK YOU ARE THE ONLY ONE WHO CAN SPEAK FOR GOD? DIDN'T GOD CALL AARON TO BE THE HIGH PRIEST? AND DON'T FORGET, I AM A PROPHETESS, TOO!

BEFORE MOSES CAN ANSWER, GOD CALLS THE THREE OF THEM TO THE TABERNACLE.

THEN GOD SPEAKS FROM A CLOUD, AND TELLS THEM THAT HE HAS CHOSEN MOSES TO LEAD THE PEOPLE OF ISRAEL. WHEN THE CLOUD DISAPPEARS, MIRIAM AND AARON GET THE SHOCK OF THEIR LIVES.

Revolt

FROM NUMBERS 12: 11—14: 10

IN A FIT OF JEALOUSY, MIRIAM AND AARON ACCUSE THEIR BROTHER, MOSES, OF ACTING AS IF HE WERE GOD'S ONLY SPOKESMAN. GOD ANSWERS THEIR ANGRY WORDS AND TELLS MIRIAM AND AARON THAT MOSES IS HIS CHOSEN LEADER. WHEN GOD FINISHES SPEAKING, MIRIAM DISCOVERS THAT SHE HAS LEPROSY—THE DISEASE MOST DREADED BY THE ISRAELITES.

OH! NO! WHY DID I SPEAK AGAINST MOSES? HELP ME! HELP ME!

WE WERE WRONG, MOSES. BUT DO NOT HOLD IT AGAINST US— PLEASE! CAN'T YOU HELP MIRIAM?

ONLY GOD CAN HEAL HER, AARON. BUT I WILL PRAY FOR OUR SISTER.

HEAL HER NOW, O GOD, I BEG OF THEE.

MIRIAM IS HEALED, BUT SHE IS BANISHED FROM THE CAMP FOR SEVEN DAYS.

ON THE SEVENTH DAY MIRIAM RETURNS, AND AARON, AS HIGH PRIEST, ACCEPTS HER BACK INTO THE CAMP.

I HAVE LEARNED MY LESSON, AARON.

SO HAVE I. LET US NEVER AGAIN DOUBT OR QUESTION GOD'S WISDOM.

THE ISRAELITES CONTINUE THEIR JOURNEY UNTIL THEY REACH THE WILDERNESS OF PARAN. THERE MOSES ORDERS THEM TO SET UP CAMP.

MEDITERRANEAN SEA

EGYPT

RED SEA

MT. SINAI

MIDIAN

CAMP
WILDERNESS
OF PARAN

CANAAN

JORDAN R.

SEA OF GALILEE

DEAD SEA

ARABIAN DESERT

MOSES CALLS A MAN FROM EACH OF THE TRIBES TO ATTEND AN IMPORTANT MEETING.

WE ARE ON THE BORDER OF CANAAN, THE LAND GOD HAS PROMISED TO US. BUT BEFORE WE GO INTO IT, WE MUST KNOW WHAT LIES AHEAD.

WHAT ARE YOUR PLANS?

WE NEED TO EXPLORE THE LAND, JOSHUA. WE MUST FIND OUT WHAT THE PEOPLE ARE LIKE, HOW MANY RIVERS WE WILL HAVE TO CROSS, HOW WELL THE CITIES ARE FORTIFIED. IT'S A DANGEROUS JOB...BUT IT MUST BE DONE.

EACH MAN HERE CAN ACT AS A SCOUT, AND WE'LL GET STARTED RIGHT AWAY.

AT DAYBREAK THE SCOUTS SET OUT— SPREADING OUT TO COVER THE MAIN AREAS OF THE LAND BEFORE THEM.

LOOK AT THAT CITY!

AND THE SIZE OF THOSE WALLS!

155

156

Rebellion

FROM **NUMBERS** 14: 10—16: 5

JOSHUA PLEADS WITH THE PEOPLE TO HAVE COURAGE AND TAKE CANAAN, THE LAND GOD HAS PROMISED THEM. BUT THE PEOPLE ARE FRIGHTENED BY THE TEN COWARDLY SCOUTS WHO REPORT GIANTS AND FORTIFIED CITIES. ANGRILY THE PEOPLE TURN AGAINST JOSHUA AND HIS FELLOW SCOUT, CALEB.

STONE THEM!

DOWN WITH JOSHUA!

BUT SUDDENLY...

LOOK OVER THERE—THE TABERNACLE IS BURNING!

DON'T BE AFRAID—THE TABERNACLE IS **NOT** ON FIRE. IT GLOWS LIKE THAT BECAUSE GOD IS THERE TALKING TO MOSES.

158

PLANS ARE QUICKLY MADE, AND THE MEN GO TO TELL MOSES.

YOU CAN GO BACK TO THE WILDERNESS, BUT WE'RE GOING ON TO CANAAN.

NO! DON'T TRY IT. GOD IS NOT WITH YOU, SO YOU CAN'T WIN.

WAIT AND SEE!

AN ARMY IS FORMED—AND SETS OUT AT ONCE TO CONQUER CANAAN.

WE FOUGHT OFF RAIDERS—WE CAN CONQUER THIS LAND.

AND WITHOUT MOSES, TOO!

BUT AS THEY GO UP A HILL, THE DEFENDING ARMY ATTACKS!

159

THIS IS A MASSACRE! LET'S GET OUT OF HERE!

IF WE GET BACK ALIVE, I'LL OBEY EVERY WORD MOSES SAYS.

THE BATTLE IS SOON OVER—THE DEFEATED ISRAELITES LIMP BACK TO CAMP.

WHAT HAPPENED?

WE DIDN'T HAVE A CHANCE. THE ENEMY CAME AT US FROM EVERY DIRECTION. OUR LEADERS WERE THE FIRST TO RUN.

THE PEOPLE SEE THE RESULTS OF DISOBEDIENCE—AND FOR A TIME THEY GLADLY FOLLOW MOSES.

BUT THEN A MAN NAMED KORAH AND SOME OF THE OTHER HELPERS IN THE TABERNACLE GROW JEALOUS OF MOSES' LEADERSHIP.

WE ARE AS GOOD AS MOSES! WHY SHOULD HE TELL US WHAT TO DO?

LET'S TELL MOSES WE'LL RUN OUR OWN AFFAIRS!

KORAH AND HIS FOLLOWERS GO TO MOSES...AND MOSES CALLS ALL THE PEOPLE TOGETHER.

TOMORROW THE LORD WILL SHOW US WHOM HE HAS CHOSEN TO LEAD OUR PEOPLE!

Serpents in the Wilderness

FROM NUMBERS 16: 5—21: 6

KORAH AND SOME OF HIS FRIENDS LED A REVOLT AGAINST MOSES AND MOSES PROMISED THEM THAT ON THE FOLLOWING DAY GOD WOULD POINT OUT HIS CHOSEN LEADER. THE MOMENT HAS COME...

DEPART FROM KORAH AND THE MEN WHO WOULD LEAD YOU TO EVIL, LEST YOU LOSE YOUR LIVES. IF GOD HAS CHOSEN ME TO LEAD YOU, THE EARTH WILL OPEN AND SWALLOW THEM UP...

AS MOSES SPEAKS, THERE IS A GREAT EARTHQUAKE, AND THE TENTS OF KORAH AND HIS FOLLOWERS FALL INTO A DEEP CRACK IN THE EARTH

THE FRIGHTENED PEOPLE TURN ONCE AGAIN TO MOSES. AS GOD COMMANDED, MOSES LEADS THEM AWAY FROM THE PROMISED LAND... TO WANDER FOR YEARS IN THE WILDERNESS.

WHEN HARDSHIPS COME, THEY FORGET THAT IT WAS THEIR FEAR THAT KEPT THEM FROM TAKING THE GOOD LAND GOD HAD PROMISED THEM. AGAIN AND AGAIN THEY COMPLAIN...

NO WATER! NOW WHAT WILL I DO?

THE SPRING IS DRY! HOW CAN I COOK— OR WASH?

OUR TRIBAL LEADERS WILL TAKE THIS UP WITH MOSES!

WELL, MOSES, WHERE ARE WE GOING TO GET WATER?

DID YOU LEAD US OUT HERE TO DIE OF THIRST?

LET'S GO BACK TO EGYPT—AT LEAST WE HAD FOOD AND WATER THERE.

ONCE AGAIN, MOSES AND HIS BROTHER, AARON, TAKE THEIR PROBLEM TO GOD. AND GOD TELLS THEM EXACTLY WHAT TO DO.

BUT MOSES IS STILL SO ANGRY WITH HIS PEOPLE THAT HE DISREGARDS GOD'S COMMAND AND STRIKES THE ROCK—TWICE—INSTEAD OF SPEAKING TO IT. WATER GUSHES OUT, AND THE PEOPLE DRINK HAPPILY.

BUT GOD IS DISPLEASED. HOW CAN MOSES AND AARON TEACH THE PEOPLE TO OBEY GOD IF THEY THEMSELVES DO NOT FOLLOW GOD'S INSTRUCTIONS? BECAUSE OF THE BAD EXAMPLE THEY HAVE SET, GOD TELLS THEM THAT NEITHER ONE SHALL ENTER THE PROMISED LAND.

THE ISRAELITES TRAVEL ON. WHEN THEY COME TO MOUNT HOR, GOD TELLS MOSES THAT AARON WILL SOON DIE, AND THAT HE SHOULD TAKE AARON AND HIS SON, ELEAZAR, TO THE MOUNTAINTOP.

ELEAZAR WILL TAKE YOUR PLACE AS HIGH PRIEST, AARON. I WILL PUT YOUR ROBES ON HIM.

AARON DIES ON MOUNT HOR, AND THE ISRAELITES MOURN FOR THIRTY DAYS. THEN THEY MOVE ON. A CLOUD LEADS THEM BY DAY, AND A PILLAR OF FIRE BY NIGHT.

164

A Giant's Boast

FROM NUMBERS 21: 7-33

HELP ME—OR I'LL DIE!

MOSES, WE HAVE SINNED— AGAINST GOD AND AGAINST YOU. FORGIVE US—AND TAKE AWAY THESE SERPENTS. PLEASE!

I WILL ASK GOD TO HELP YOU.

MOSES PRAYS AND GOD DIRECTS HIM TO MAKE A SERPENT OF BRASS AND PUT IT ON A POLE.

LISTEN TO ME, ALL YOU WHO HAVE BEEN BITTEN BY THE SNAKES. GOD HAS SAID THAT IF YOU LOOK AT THIS BRASS SERPENT, YOU WILL BE WELL AGAIN.

166

167

AT DAYBREAK—KING SIHON STRIKES AND IS MET WITH A SURPRISE COUNTERATTACK FROM THE ISRAELITES.

THE AMORITES ARE DEFEATED IN A SWIFT BATTLE. THEN JOSHUA GOES ON TO TAKE THE ENEMY'S CAPITAL CITY OF HESHBON.

THE ISRAELITE SOLDIERS ARE EAGER TO PUSH ON, AFTER THIS VICTORY, BUT JOSHUA GOES TO MOSES FOR ADVICE.

SHALL WE MOVE NORTH INTO BASHAN? IT IS A POWERFUL COUNTRY WITH A GIANT FOR A KING.

SEND OUT SOME SCOUTS TO EXPLORE THE LAND FIRST, JOSHUA. THEN WE WILL DECIDE.

JOSHUA'S SCOUTS ARE DISCOVERED, AND A MESSENGER HURRIES TO TELL KING OG OF BASHAN.

O KING, I SAW SOME STRANGE MEN SPYING OUT OUR LAND.

THEY MUST BE THE ISRAELITES. THEY'VE JUST CONQUERED THE AMORITES, BUT **WE'LL** TEACH THEM A LESSON...

168

A New Leader

BOLDLY THE GIANT KING OG OF BASHAN SETS OUT TO TEACH THE ISRAELITES A LESSON IN WARFARE. BUT HE SOON FINDS HE IS NO MATCH FOR JOSHUA. OG'S ARMY IS BEATEN. HE TRIES TO ESCAPE...

AFTER HIM, MEN! CATCH HIM!

THE KING IS CAPTURED, AND THE ISRAELITES TAKE THE COUNTRY.

AFTER CONQUERING THE AMORITES AND BASHAN, THE ISRAELITES SET UP THEIR TENTS ON THE PLAINS OF MOAB.

MEDITERRANEAN SEA
SEA OF GALILEE
BASHAN
JORDAN RIVER
RIVER JABBOK
CANAAN
PLAINS OF MOAB
AMORITES
AMMONITES
JERICHO •
RIVER ARNON
DEAD SEA
MOAB
BROOK ZERED

OUR THREE TRIBES ARE READY TO SETTLE DOWN HERE AND BUILD OUR HOMES. DO WE HAVE YOUR PERMISSION?

YOU HELPED TO CONQUER THIS LAND, AND YOU MAY HAVE IT. BUT FIRST WE'LL NEED YOU TO HELP US CONQUER THE LAND THAT LIES AHEAD.

WE'LL HELP, MOSES.

YES, YOU CAN COUNT ON US.

FOR THE SECOND TIME THE ISRAELITES HAVE COME TO THE BORDER OF THE PROMISED LAND. THIS TIME THEY ARE NOT AFRAID. MEN TALK OF THE FLOCKS AND HERDS THEY WILL HAVE...AND WOMEN DREAM OF PEACEFUL HOMES IN THE LAND WHICH GOD HAS PROMISED THEM.

ONE DAY MOSES CALLS JOSHUA TO AN IMPORTANT MEETING...

GOD HAS TOLD ME THAT MY WORK HERE ON EARTH IS ALMOST FINISHED, JOSHUA. A NEW LEADER WILL TAKE OUR PEOPLE INTO THE PROMISED LAND.

A NEW LEADER? OH, NO, MOSES! WHO COULD EVER TAKE YOUR PLACE?

YOU— JOSHUA!

THE AGED LEADER CLIMBS MOUNT NEBO AND GAZES DOWN ON THE LAND GOD HAS PROMISED HIS PEOPLE—AND THERE—ALONE WITH GOD—HE DIES.

BACK IN CAMP JOSHUA PRAYS TO GOD FOR HELP, AND THE LORD ANSWERS: BE NOT AFRAID, FOR THE LORD THY GOD IS WITH THEE.

THE ISRAELITES MOURN THIRTY DAYS FOR MOSES. THEN, JOSHUA CALLS A MEETING.

THE CAMPAIGNS AHEAD WILL BE HARD AND DANGEROUS. BUT I'LL SEEK GOD'S GUIDANCE IN EVERYTHING WE DO.

AND WE WILL FOLLOW YOU AS WE DID MOSES!

THREE DAYS FROM NOW WE WILL CROSS THE JORDAN RIVER. THEN WE MUST CAPTURE THE CITY OF JERICHO—BUT FIRST WE NEED TO LEARN ALL WE CAN ABOUT IT.

172

Crossing the Jordan

FROM JOSHUA 2: 1—4: 10

WHEN JOSHUA'S TWO SPIES ENTER JERICHO THEY AVOID THE PUBLIC INN AND SEEK LODGING IN THE HOUSE OF A WOMAN NAMED RAHAB.

WE ARE STRANGERS IN YOUR CITY—MAY WE HAVE A ROOM HERE FOR THE NIGHT?

YES—

THE KING'S SOLDIER IS SUSPICIOUS OF THESE MEN! I'LL FIND OUT WHAT BRINGS THEM HERE.

LATER... DO YOU KNOW THAT YOU HAVE BEEN FOLLOWED?

FOLLOWED— BY WHOM?

THE SPIES PROMISE SAFETY TO RAHAB AND HER FAMILY.

175

Siege of Jericho

FROM JOSHUA 4: 1—6: 20

As IF HELD BACK BY A GIANT HAND, THE WATERS OF THE JORDAN STOP FLOWING WHILE THE ISRAELITES CROSS OVER INTO THE PROMISED LAND. WHEN ALL HAVE CROSSED, JOSHUA ORDERS A MAN FROM EACH OF THE TRIBES TO BRING A LARGE STONE FROM THE RIVER BED.

CARRY THESE STONES TO CAMP. THEY WILL REMIND US OF HOW GOD STOPPED THE JORDAN SO THAT WE MIGHT CROSS OVER SAFELY.

THEN JOSHUA SETS UP 12 OTHER STONES IN THE MIDDLE OF THE JORDAN — AT THE PLACE WHERE THE PRIESTS HOLD THE ARK. AFTER THAT HE COMMANDS THE PRIESTS TO CARRY THE ARK ACROSS. WHEN THEY REACH THE BANK THE FLOOD WATERS OF THE JORDAN RUSH FORTH...

THE ISRAELITES SET UP THEIR FIRST CAMP AT GILGAL—AND HERE THEY CELEBRATE THEIR FIRST PASSOVER FEAST IN THE PROMISED LAND.

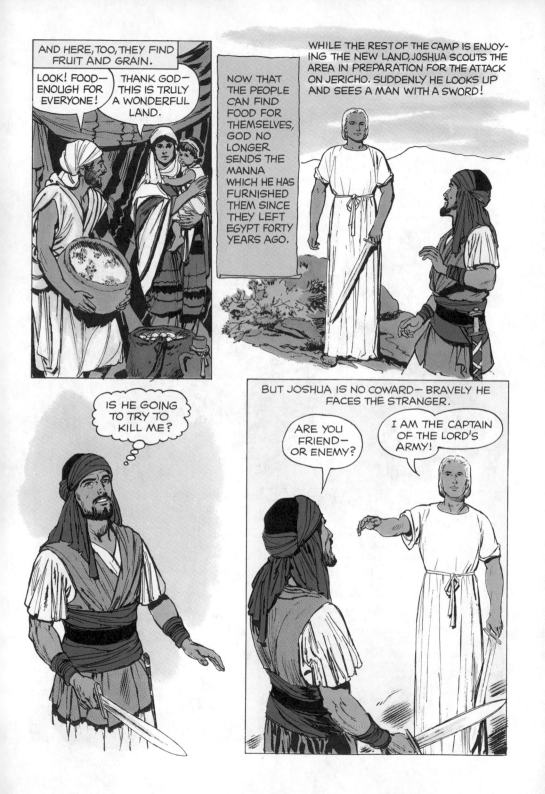

AND HERE, TOO, THEY FIND FRUIT AND GRAIN.

LOOK! FOOD— ENOUGH FOR EVERYONE!

THANK GOD— THIS IS TRULY A WONDERFUL LAND.

NOW THAT THE PEOPLE CAN FIND FOOD FOR THEMSELVES, GOD NO LONGER SENDS THE MANNA WHICH HE HAS FURNISHED THEM SINCE THEY LEFT EGYPT FORTY YEARS AGO.

WHILE THE REST OF THE CAMP IS ENJOY- ING THE NEW LAND, JOSHUA SCOUTS THE AREA IN PREPARATION FOR THE ATTACK ON JERICHO. SUDDENLY HE LOOKS UP AND SEES A MAN WITH A SWORD!

IS HE GOING TO TRY TO KILL ME?

BUT JOSHUA IS NO COWARD— BRAVELY HE FACES THE STRANGER.

ARE YOU FRIEND— OR ENEMY?

I AM THE CAPTAIN OF THE LORD'S ARMY!

179

Attack that Failed

FROM JOSHUA 6: 20—7: 4

ONCE EACH DAY FOR SIX DAYS THE ISRAELITES HAVE MARCHED AROUND THE CITY OF JERICHO. NOW, ON THE SEVENTH DAY, JOSHUA ORDERS THEM TO MARCH AROUND SEVEN TIMES. THE PRIESTS BLOW THEIR TRUMPETS—THE MARCHERS SHOUT—AND THE WALLS OF THE MIGHTY CITY FALL FLAT.

JERICHO IS OURS!

FIND RAHAB, THE WOMAN WHO PROTECTED YOU WHEN YOU SCOUTED OUT THE CITY. BRING HER AND HER FAMILY TO OUR CAMP.

FIGHTING THEIR WAY THROUGH THE RUBBLE AND DUST, THE TWO SCOUTS SEARCH OUT THE HOUSE OF RAHAB.

LOOK—THERE'S THE RED ROPE IN THE WINDOW!

EVERYTHING IN THE CITY WILL BE DESTROYED. BUT YOU AND YOUR FAMILY WILL BE SAFE AT OUR CAMP AS WE PROMISED YOU. COME—

THANK GOD.

MEANTIME THE ISRAELITE SOLDIERS SEARCH THE CITY FOR IRON, BRASS, SILVER AND GOLD FOR THE TABERNACLE TREASURY.

LOOK AT THIS BEAUTIFUL ROBE—

FORGET IT— JOSHUA SAID NO ONE WAS TO KEEP ANYTHING FOR HIMSELF.

BUT ONE SOLDIER, ACHAN, COVETS THE THINGS HE SEES.

WHY SHOULD I FIGHT FOR A CITY AND NOT TAKE SOME OF THE SPOIL? I'LL HIDE THESE, AND NO ONE WILL KNOW...

THAT NIGHT WHILE THE REST OF THE CAMP SLEEPS HE BURIES HIS STOLEN TREASURE.

THIS WILL HELP ME GET STARTED IN THIS NEW LAND.

FINALLY JERICHO IS SET ON FIRE... AND FROM A DISTANT HILLTOP JOSHUA AND HIS MEN WATCH.

SOON THERE WILL BE NOTHING LEFT OF A ONCE POWERFUL CITY.

IT WAS SO WICKED THAT IT HAD TO BE DESTROYED OR ITS EVIL WAYS WOULD HAVE SPREAD AMONG OUR PEOPLE.

THE NEXT DAY, JOSHUA CALLS SOME OF HIS SCOUTS TO HIM.

HERE LIES THE CITY OF AI—IT GUARDS THE APPROACH TO OUR FUTURE CAMPAIGNS. WE MUST FIND OUT HOW STRONG THE CITY IS BEFORE WE ATTACK IT.

WE'LL SCOUT IT OUT AS WE DID JERICHO.

JOSHUA'S MEN LOSE NO TIME IN APPROACHING IT.

GREETINGS! WE'RE GOING TO AI—IS IT A BIG CITY?

I'D SAY ABOUT 12,000, AND THAT INCLUDES A SMALL ARMY.

THE SCOUTS RETURN TO CAMP, EAGER TO GIVE THEIR GOOD NEWS TO JOSHUA.

THE ARMY OF AI IS SMALL. WE CAN TAKE THE CITY AND LEAVE MOST OF OUR TROOPS HERE TO REST.

JOSHUA TAKES THE ADVICE OF HIS SCOUTS AND SENDS ONLY 3,000 MEN TO TAKE AI.

THIS WILL BE EASY!

BUT AT THE GATES OF THE CITY...

HO, LOOK AT THEM RUN. THEY'RE AFRAID TO FIGHT.

SO THESE ARE THE BRAVE ISRAELITES WHO TOOK JERICHO!

Tricked

FROM JOSHUA 7: 5—9: 16

THE FRIGHTENED ISRAELITES RETURN FROM THEIR DEFEAT AT AI. JOSHUA AND THE WHOLE CAMP ARE STUNNED!

WHAT HAPPENED?

I DON'T KNOW—ALL OF A SUDDEN I WAS AFRAID—AND RAN.

IT WAS AWFUL! THE SOLDIERS OF AI CHASED US ALL THE WAY TO THE STONE QUARRIES.

BUT WHY? WHY WERE YOU AFRAID? WHY DID YOU RUN?

THE SOLDIERS CANNOT ANSWER, SO JOSHUA SEEKS HELP FROM GOD.

O GOD, WHY DID THIS HAPPEN TO US? NOW OUR ENEMIES WILL DESTROY US.

GOD REPLIES THAT THE PEOPLE ARE BEING PUNISHED BECAUSE SOMEONE DISOBEYED HIM WHEN THEY TOOK JERICHO.

EARLY THE NEXT MORNING JOSHUA CALLS THE LEADERS OF THE TRIBES TO HIM.

SOMEONE DISOBEYED GOD'S ORDER AND KEPT PART OF THE SPOILS OF JERICHO FOR HIMSELF. THAT MAN MUST BE PUNISHED— OR WE WILL DIE AT THE HANDS OF THE ENEMY.

GOD POINTS OUT ACHAN AS THE GUILTY ONE.

IT IS TRUE—I SINNED AGAINST GOD AND MY PEOPLE.

NOW WE STAND RIGHT WITH GOD.

THAT SAME DAY JOSHUA CALLS HIS LEADERS TO HIM AGAIN.

TAKE THIRTY THOUSAND MEN AND HIDE THEM WEST OF AI. DO NOT ATTACK UNTIL I GIVE THE SIGNAL.

UNDER COVER OF DARKNESS THE ISRAELITES HIDE OUT AROUND AI.

WHAT IS JOSHUA'S PLAN?

I DON'T KNOW —BUT THIS TIME I'M NOT AFRAID. WITH GOD'S HELP WE WILL NOT FAIL.

EARLY THE NEXT MORNING, JOSHUA LEADS SOME OF HIS SOLDIERS AGAINST AI. REMEMBERING HOW THEY HAD CHASED THE ISRAELITES AWAY BEFORE, THE SOLDIERS OF AI RUSH OUT OF THE CITY GATE.

LET'S WIPE THEM OUT THIS TIME!

JOSHUA RAISES HIS SPEAR—IT IS THE SIGNAL FOR THE ISRAELITES IN AMBUSH. THEY RUSH IN AND SET FIRE TO THE CITY. THE SOLDIERS OF AI ARE CAUGHT IN A TRAP BETWEEN THE FORCES OF ISRAEL AND ARE QUICKLY DEFEATED.

THE NEWS OF JOSHUA'S VICTORIES SPREADS THROUGHOUT THE LAND, AND IN NEARBY GIBEON...

THE ISRAELITES WILL PROBABLY ATTACK US NEXT.

I KNOW OF A WAY WE CAN OUTSMART THEM. LISTEN TO THIS—

THE NEXT DAY TWO MEN FROM GIBEON, DRESSED IN DUSTY, TATTERED CLOTHES, STOP AT THE ISRAELITE CAMP.

GREETINGS. WHERE ARE YOU FROM?

FROM A FAR COUNTRY— SEE, THESE CLOTHES WERE NEW WHEN WE LEFT HOME.

WHY HAVE YOU COME TO SEE US?

WE HAVE HEARD OF THE GREATNESS OF THE LORD YOUR GOD. WE WANT TO SIGN A PEACE TREATY WITH YOU.

JOSHUA BELIEVES THEM AND PROMISES TO LIVE IN PEACE WITH THEIR PEOPLE.

BUT THREE DAYS LATER—

JOSHUA, I FOLLOWED THOSE MEN— THEY LIVE IN GIBEON, THE CITY WE PLANNED TO ATTACK!

WE'VE BEEN TRICKED! LET'S ATTACK THE CITY AT ONCE!

NO, I SHALL KEEP MY WORD, BUT...

188

Forced March

FROM JOSHUA 9: 17—11: 7

JOSHUA HAS BEEN TRICKED INTO AN ALLIANCE WITH GIBEON. BUT HE DOES NOT KNOW THAT THE RULERS OF FIVE OTHER CITIES HAVE LEARNED OF THE ALLIANCE, TOO, AND ARE PLOTTING REVENGE.

THE ISRAELITES ARE GETTING TOO POWERFUL. WE SHOULD TEACH GIBEON A LESSON FOR JOINING WITH THEM.

I AGREE. IF WE TAKE GIBEON WE'LL HAVE ANOTHER FORTIFIED CITY IN CASE THE ISRAELITES ATTACK US.

THE ARMIES OF THE FIVE KINGS MARCH AT ONCE ON GIBEON.

TAKE WORD TO JOSHUA—TELL HIM WE'RE BEING ATTACKED AND NEED HELP.

IN THE CAMP OF JOSHUA...

GIBEON HAS BEEN ATTACKED. WE ASK THAT YOU REMEMBER YOUR ALLIANCE WITH OUR CITY.

ISRAEL WILL KEEP ITS WORD.

190

Traitors to God

FROM JOSHUA 11: 8—JUDGES 4: 2

WHEN JOSHUA LEARNS THAT THE NORTHERN KINGS ARE FORMING A GREAT ARMY, HE MAKES A QUICK MARCH NORTH AND CATCHES THEM OFF GUARD. HIS LIGHTNING ATTACK THROWS THE ENEMY INTO PANIC.

WHAT HAPPENED?

WE'VE BEEN ATTACKED!

WE'RE SURROUNDED!

WITH QUICK, DECISIVE BLOWS, JOSHUA TAKES THE CAMP. SOME OF THE ENEMY TRY TO ESCAPE, BUT ISRAELITE SOLDIERS FOLLOW IN CLOSE PURSUIT. THE FIGHTING LASTS THROUGHOUT THE DAY, BUT BY NIGHTFALL THE ENEMY IS IN JOSHUA'S HANDS.

WHEN THE WAR IS OVER, THE ISRAELITES REJOICE AND GIVE THANKS TO GOD FOR THEIR VICTORIES. THEN JOSHUA CALLS THE LEADERS TO A SPECIAL MEETING.

WE HAVE WON MUCH OF THE LAND GOD PROMISED US; IT IS TIME FOR US TO DIVIDE IT AMONG THE TRIBES.

JOSHUA DIES, AND FOR A LONG TIME HIS LEADERS KEEP THEIR PLEDGE TO GOD. THEY BUILD UP STRONG CITIES AND JUDGES ARE CHOSEN TO RULE OVER THEM. BUT WHEN JOSHUA'S FRIENDS GROW OLD AND DIE, MANY OF THE ISRAELITES FORGET GOD...

AND BEGIN TO WORSHIP THE IDOLS OF THEIR NEIGHBORS...

AS A RESULT, THE ISRAELITES BECOME SO WEAK THAT THEY CANNOT DEFEND THEMSELVES AGAINST THE ATTACKS OF THEIR NEIGHBORS. TIME AND AGAIN ISRAELITE JUDGES LEAD THEIR PEOPLE BACK TO GOD AND VICTORY. BUT THE PEOPLE'S FAITH IS WEAK; WHEN THEY TURN AGAIN TO WORSHIP HEATHEN IDOLS THEY ARE INVADED BY KING JABIN'S RAIDERS...

Battle in the Storm

FROM JUDGES 4—5

AGAIN THE ISRAELITES FORGET ALL THAT GOD HAS DONE FOR THEM AND TURN TO WORSHIP THE IDOLS OF THEIR NEIGHBORS. SOON THEY BECOME SO WEAK AND AFRAID THEY CAN'T EVEN PROTECT THEIR OWN FIELDS FROM CANAANITE RAIDERS.

STOP! THAT'S MY GRAIN!

IT'S OURS NOW—SO, WHAT ARE YOU GOING TO DO ABOUT IT?

YEARS AGO OUR GREAT LEADER, JOSHUA, CONQUERED THE CANAANITES. NOW THEY ARE CONQUERING US!

WHAT'S THE MATTER WITH OUR LEADERS? WE'LL STARVE IF KING JABIN'S MEN KEEP STEALING OUR GRAIN.

ONE FIELD AFTER ANOTHER IS RAIDED UNTIL AT LAST THE FARMERS HAVE A MEETING.

SOMETHING MUST BE DONE—AT ONCE— TO STOP THOSE CANAANITES.

LET'S GO IN A BODY TO SEE DEBORAH.

THE ANGRY FARMERS TAKE THEIR STORY TO DEBORAH, WHO IS THE JUDGE OF ISRAEL.

WHAT CAN WE DO—THE CANAANITES ARE STEALING ALL OUR FOOD.

GOD WILL HELP US—IF WE TRUST HIM.

DEBORAH ACTS SWIFTLY...

TAKE A MESSAGE TO CAPTAIN BARAK IN THE NORTH COUNTRY. TELL HIM TO COME AT ONCE.

THIS SOUNDS LIKE WAR.

WE DON'T HAVE A CHANCE AGAINST THE CANAANITES. THEY HAVE NINE HUNDRED CHARIOTS, AND WE HAVE ONLY A FEW CRUDE WEAPONS.

A FEW DAYS LATER...

BARAK—THIS IS THE PLAN GOD HAS GIVEN ME. TAKE TEN THOUSAND MEN TO MOUNT TABOR. WHEN KING JABIN HEARS OF THIS HE WILL ORDER HIS ARMY, UNDER SISERA, TO COME OUT AND DESTROY US, BUT WITH GOD'S HELP YOU CAN DEFEAT THEM.

I'LL LEAD THE ARMY, BUT ONLY IF YOU'LL GO WITH US. GOD SPEAKS THROUGH YOU, AND IF YOU ARE THERE, I KNOW GOD WILL HELP US.

I'LL GO, BUT BECAUSE YOU DID NOT HAVE THE FAITH TO LEAD BY YOURSELF, BARAK, YOU WILL NOT GET THE CREDIT FOR THE VICTORY. GOD WILL DELIVER JABIN'S GENERAL, SISERA, INTO THE HAND OF A WOMAN.

AFTER A QUICK MARCH, THE ISRAELITES REACH MOUNT TABOR. DEBORAH'S PROPHECY COMES TRUE—THE CANAANITE ARMY COMES TO MEET THEM.

HAVE FAITH— FOR THIS IS THE DAY THE LORD WILL DELIVER US!

DEBORAH GIVES THE SIGNAL...AND BARAK CHARGES DOWN THE MOUNTAIN AT THE HEAD OF HIS TROOPS. ABOVE THEM LIGHTNING FLASHES...

A CLOUDBURST TURNS THE PLAIN INTO A SEA OF MUD. THE IRON CHARIOTS OF THE CANAANITES SINK INTO THE MIRE. TRAPPED, THEY ARE AT THE MERCY OF THE ISRAELITES, WHO ATTACK WITH SPEED AND COURAGE.

196

THE CANAANITES RETREAT.

TO THE RIVER!

WHEN SISERA, GENERAL OF THE CANAANITE FORCES, SEES THAT THEY HAVE BEEN DEFEATED, HE TRIES TO ESCAPE TO A DISTANT CITY. ON THE WAY HE STOPS TO REST IN WHAT HE THINKS IS A FRIENDLY TENT. BUT THE WOMAN WHO LIVES THERE, NAMED JAEL, IS LOYAL TO ISRAEL AND KILLS SISERA WHILE HE IS ASLEEP.

BUT THE KISHON RIVER IS ALREADY OVERFLOWING ITS BANKS... AND THE CANAANITES WHO TRY TO SWIM TO SAFETY SINK UNDER THE WEIGHT OF THEIR HEAVY ARMOR.

WHEN DEBORAH LEARNS THAT THE CANAANITES HAVE BEEN DEFEATED, SHE SINGS A SONG OF VICTORY...

I WILL SING UNTO THE LORD; I WILL SING PRAISES TO THE LORD GOD OF ISRAEL.

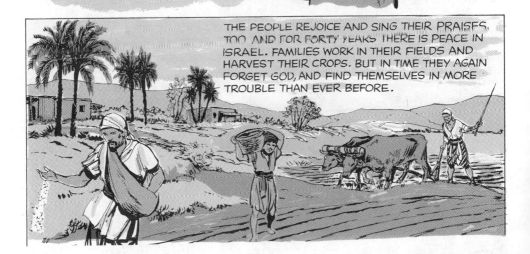

THE PEOPLE REJOICE AND SING THEIR PRAISES, TOO. AND FOR FORTY YEARS THERE IS PEACE IN ISRAEL. FAMILIES WORK IN THEIR FIELDS AND HARVEST THEIR CROPS. BUT IN TIME THEY AGAIN FORGET GOD, AND FIND THEMSELVES IN MORE TROUBLE THAN EVER BEFORE.

Angry Mob of Baal

FROM JUDGES 6: 1—30

IN THE YEARS OF PLENTY THAT FOLLOW DEBORAH'S VICTORY OVER THE CANAANITES, THE ISRAELITES AGAIN FORGET GOD. ONE BY ONE THEY JOIN THEIR NEIGHBORS IN WORSHIPING THE IDOL, BAAL. AT LAST ONLY A FEW MEN IN ALL ISRAEL REMEMBER THAT IT WAS GOD WHO HAD RESCUED THEM FROM THEIR ENEMIES.

ROVING BANDS OF DESERT TRIBESMEN BEGIN TO TERRORIZE THE ISRAELITE VILLAGES, AND RAID THE FIELDS.

RUN FOR YOUR LIVES!

IF THEY FIND WHERE I HID MY GRAIN, WE'LL STARVE.

WHEN THE RAID IS OVER...

IT'S GONE—MY GRAIN, IT'S GONE!

FOR SEVEN LONG YEARS THE ISRAELITES SUFFER AT THE HANDS OF THE DESERT TRIBESMEN. THEY HIDE OUT IN CAVES, THRESH THEIR GRAIN IN SECRET PLACES...BUT ALWAYS THE RAIDERS RETURN.

THEN EVEN MORE FRIGHTENING NEWS COMES...

THE MIDIANITES ARE COMING AGAIN. AND WITH THEM GREAT HORDES FROM THE EAST.

LIKE GRASSHOPPERS THE ENEMY SWARMS OVER THE ISRAELITE FIELDS...STEALING GRAIN, CATTLE, AND SHEEP.

ONE DAY A YOUNG ISRAELITE IS SECRETLY THRESHING HIS GRAIN WHEN A STRANGER APPEARS BEFORE HIM.

WHO ARE YOU? AND WHAT DO YOU WANT?

GOD HAS CHOSEN YOU, GIDEON, TO SAVE YOUR PEOPLE.

BUT GIDEON IS STILL NOT SURE THAT HE HAS BEEN CALLED BY GOD. HE ASKS FOR A SIGN.

IF IN THE MORNING THIS WOOL IS WET WITH DEW AND THE GROUND IS DRY, THEN I'LL KNOW THAT I AM THE ONE CHOSEN BY GOD.

THE NEXT MORNING GIDEON HAS HIS SIGN...

THE GROUND IS DRY— BUT THERE'S ENOUGH DEW ON THIS WOOL TO FILL A WHOLE BOWL.

BUT GIDEON IS STILL AFRAID...

O GOD, GIVE ME ONE MORE SIGN. IF IN THE MORNING THE WOOL IS DRY AND THE GROUND IS WET, THEN I'LL KNOW.

THE NEXT MORNING...

THE WOOL IS DRY—AND THE GROUND IS WET! NOW I KNOW THAT I AM THE ONE CALLED TO SAVE MY PEOPLE!

ONLY THREE HUNDRED MEN ARE LEFT OUT OF GIDEON'S ARMY OF 32,000 MEN. NOW THE ISRAELITES KNOW BEYOND ALL DOUBT THAT ONLY WITH GOD'S HELP CAN THEY DEFEAT THE ENEMY.

HIDE YOUR TORCHES IN THESE PITCHERS. SPREAD OUT ON THREE SIDES OF THE CAMP. LISTEN FOR MY SIGNAL ON THE TRUMPET.

WE'RE READY.

AT GIDEON'S SIGNAL, THE MEN BLOW THEIR TRUMPETS, SMASH THEIR PITCHERS, WAVE THEIR TORCHES, GIVE THE BATTLE CRY...

THE SWORD OF THE LORD AND OF GIDEON!

AND CHARGE DOWN THE HILL— THREE HUNDRED AGAINST THOUSANDS!

Philistine Raiders

FROM JUDGES 7: 22—13: 1

THE STILLNESS OF THE NIGHT IS SUDDENLY BROKEN BY THE BLARE OF 300 TRUMPETS AND CRASH OF BROKEN PITCHERS. STARTLED FROM THEIR SLEEP, THE MIDIANITES RUSH OUT TO FIND THEIR CAMP ABLAZE WITH FLAMING TORCHES. IN THEIR PANIC THEY EVEN ATTACK ONE ANOTHER...BUT GIDEON AND HIS 300 ISRAELITES SURROUND THEM.

WE'VE BEEN ATTACKED!

WHERE'S MY SWORD— MY SHIELD?

THE MIDIANITES THINK THEY HAVE BEEN ATTACKED BY A GIANT ARMY...AND IN TERROR MANY TRY TO ESCAPE TO THE RIVER.

TAKE WORD TO THE TRIBE OF EPHRAIM TO HOLD THE FORDS OF THE JORDAN.

SOME OF THE MIDIANITES REACH THE JORDAN RIVER—BUT THEY ARE CAPTURED BY ISRAELITE SOLDIERS FROM EPHRAIM WAITING IN AMBUSH.

IN THE NORTH, GIDEON CHASES THE ENEMY ACROSS THE JORDAN...AND AT LAST ALL OF THE MIDIANITE FORCES ARE DEFEATED.

Attacked by a Lion

FROM JUDGES 13: 2—14: 5

THE PHILISTINE RAIDERS STRIKE TIME AND AGAIN AT THE ISRAELITE VILLAGES, CARRYING OFF GRAIN, CATTLE- EVEN CHILDREN TO WORK AS SLAVES. BUT ONE ISRAELITE MOTHER AND FATHER WAIT EAGERLY FOR A STRANGE AND WONDERFUL PROMISE TO COME TRUE. ONE DAY THEY TELL THEIR YOUNG SON, SAMSON, ABOUT IT.

BEFORE YOU WERE BORN, AN ANGEL OF GOD TOLD US THAT SOME DAY YOU WOULD BE THE LEADER OF OUR PEOPLE AND SAVE US FROM THE WICKED PHILISTINES.

I WOULD SAVE OUR PEOPLE? HOW?

WE DON'T KNOW HOW, SON, BUT IF YOU TRUST IN GOD, HE WILL SHOW YOU THE WAY. BUT YOU MUST KEEP A PROMISE YOUR MOTHER MADE TO GOD.

A PROMISE? WHAT IS IT?

TO SET YOU APART AS ONE DEDICATED TO GOD, YOU WILL NEVER CUT YOUR HAIR—OR TOUCH STRONG DRINK.

SAMSON KEEPS HIS MOTHER'S PROMISE TO GOD. AND AS THE YEARS PASS AND THE PHILISTINES CONTINUE TO ROB AND PLUNDER THE ISRAELITES, HE DREAMS OF THE DAY WHEN HE CAN SAVE HIS PEOPLE. ONE DAY AFTER A RAID, HE STORMS ANGRILY INTO A MEETING OF THE ELDERS.

THEY KILLED MY COUSIN WITH THIS SPEAR! IT HAS AN IRON HEAD...

YES, THE PHILISTINES KNOW HOW TO MAKE IRON SPEARS, BUT WE DON'T. HOW CAN WE FIGHT THEM WITH WOODEN SPEARS?

SOME DAY I'LL FIGHT THEM, AND WHEN I DO...

HE SNAPPED THAT SPEAR AS IF IT WERE A TWIG.

IF HE IS THAT STRONG NOW, WHAT WILL HE BE LIKE WHEN HE IS A MAN?

AS SAMSON GROWS, HIS STRENGTH GROWS UNTIL AT LAST HE IS THE STRONGEST MAN IN ALL THE TRIBE OF DAN. SOME OF THE PEOPLE WATCH ANXIOUSLY AS HE SETS OUT ONE DAY SEEKING ADVENTURE IN A PHILISTINE VILLAGE.

I HOPE HE DOESN'T GET INTO ANY TROUBLE.

NO MAN IN HIS RIGHT MIND WOULD RISK A FIGHT WITH SAMSON.

NO—NOT ONE MAN, BUT A WHOLE VILLAGE MIGHT. AND THAT COULD MEAN TROUBLE FOR US, TOO.

IN THE VILLAGE OF TIMNATH, SAMSON MEETS A PHILISTINE GIRL.

MAY I GIVE YOU A DRINK OF WATER?

YES, THANK YOU.

SHE'S THE MOST BEAUTIFUL GIRL I'VE EVER SEEN.

IN HER COMPANY SAMSON FORGETS HIS ANGER TOWARD HER PEOPLE.

WILL YOU MEET ME HERE TOMORROW AT THE SAME TIME?

IF MY FATHER WILL LET ME.

BACK HOME SAMSON LOSES NO TIME TELLING HIS PARENTS WHAT HE WANTS.

I HAVE FALLEN IN LOVE WITH A PHILISTINE GIRL—MAKE ARRANGEMENTS WITH HER PARENTS FOR OUR MARRIAGE.

MARRIAGE WITH A PHILISTINE?

HOW CAN YOU LOVE ONE OF OUR ENEMIES? SHE DOESN'T BELIEVE IN OUR GOD!

I WANT TO MARRY HER ANYHOW.

ON THE DAY SAMSON SETS OUT FOR HIS WEDDING, HE STOPS TO EXAMINE THE BODY OF THE LION HE HAD KILLED--AND FINDS THAT BEES HAVE MADE HONEY IN THE CARCASS.

FOOD FROM A LION-- HONEY FROM THE STRONG. GIVES ME AN IDEA FOR A RIDDLE TO TRY ON THE WEDDING GUESTS.

IN TIMNATH HE IS GREETED BY A GROUP OF YOUNG MEN.

I AM YOUR BEST MAN, AND I HAVE BROUGHT 29 OF MY FRIENDS TO BE YOUR GUESTS.

GOOD! NOW WILL YOU TRY TO GUESS MY RIDDLE. IF YOU DO, I'LL GIVE EACH OF YOU A SHIRT AND A ROBE. IF YOU CAN'T, EACH OF YOU WILL GIVE ME A SHIRT AND ROBE.

WE'LL TAKE YOU UP ON THAT-- WHAT'S THE RIDDLE?

OUT OF THE EATER CAME FOOD; OUT OF THE STRONG CAME SWEETNESS. YOU HAVE A WEEK TO GUESS THE ANSWER.

BUT AS THE WEEK GOES BY, NEITHER THE BEST MAN NOR ANY OF HIS FRIENDS CAN GUESS SAMSON'S RIDDLE.

WHAT WILL WE DO? I CAN'T AFFORD TO GIVE HIM A SHIRT AND ROBE.

NEITHER CAN I. WE'LL HAVE TO GET THE ANSWER FROM HIS WIFE. AFTER ALL, SHE IS A PHILISTINE.

GET THE ANSWER FROM SAMSON, OR WE'LL SET FIRE TO YOUR FATHER'S HOUSE WITH **YOU** IN IT!

NO! NO! GIVE ME TIME.

209

Samson's Revenge

FROM JUDGES 14: 19—15: 12

SAMSON IS FURIOUS! HE HAS LOST THE WAGER OF THIRTY ROBES TO THE PHILISTINES WHO FORCED HIS WIFE TO TELL THEM THE ANSWER TO HIS RIDDLE. HE LEAVES HIS WEDDING FEAST AND ENTERS ANOTHER CITY...

AH! ENOUGH PHILISTINES TO PAY MY DEBT--AND ALL OF THEM HANDSOMELY DRESSED, TOO.

WHO HIT ME?

WHAT'S HAPPENING?

PHILISTINES TRICKED ME, SO PHILISTINES WILL PAY THE DEBT.

STILL IN A RAGE, SAMSON RETURNS TO THE WEDDING FEAST...

HERE-- THE DEBT IS PAID! AND BY THE LIVES OF YOUR OWN COUNTRYMEN!

BACK HOME AS SAMSON'S ANGER COOLS, HE THINKS OF HIS WIFE WAITING FOR HIM.

IT WASN'T HER FAULT. THEY FORCED HER TO TELL THE ANSWER. I'LL GO TO HER AND TELL HER I'M SORRY.

IN THE PHILISTINE CITY HE GOES STRAIGHT TO THE HOME OF HIS WIFE'S FATHER.

I'VE COME TO SEE MY WIFE.

YOUR WIFE? WE THOUGHT YOU HATED HER. SHE IS NOW MARRIED TO YOUR BEST MAN.

HERE IS HER YOUNGER SISTER--SHE'S EVEN MORE BEAUTIFUL. DO YOU WANT TO MARRY HER?

NO! I SHOULD HAVE KNOWN BETTER THAN TO TRUST A PHILISTINE. WHATEVER I DO NOW YOU WILL HAVE COMING TO YOU.

ON THE WAY HOME, HE GOES THROUGH FIELDS RICH WITH RIPENED GRAIN.

FIELDS AND VINEYARDS STOLEN FROM MY PEOPLE! I KNOW HOW I CAN MAKE THE PHILISTINES SORRY FOR WHAT THEY DID TO ME.

QUICKLY SAMSON SETS FOXES RACING THROUGH THE FIELDS AND VINEYARDS WITH FLAMING TORCHES. IN A MATTER OF MINUTES THE WHOLE COUNTRYSIDE IS ABLAZE.

IN THE CITY THE PHILISTINES WATCH WITH TERROR AS THE SKY GROWS RED.

SAMSON DID THIS! HE'S GETTING EVEN WITH HIS WIFE'S FATHER FOR MARRYING HER TO ANOTHER.

HER FATHER SHOULD HAVE KNOWN BETTER THAN TO TRICK SAMSON. COME ON, LET'S GIVE OUR COUNTRY-MAN A TASTE OF HIS OWN MEDICINE.

THE ANGRY PHILISTINES SET FIRE TO THE HOME OF SAMSON'S FATHER-IN-LAW...BUT THEY DO NOT COUNT ON SAMSON'S RETURN.

THAT'S MY WIFE'S HOUSE-- WHERE IS SHE?

IN THERE!

DEAD! YOU KILLED HER WHILE SHE SLEPT! IF YOU'RE SO BRAVE, SHOW IT NOW.

The Gaza Trap

FROM JUDGES 15: 13—16: 2

WHEN THE PHILISTINE ARMY DEMANDS THAT THE TRIBE OF JUDAH TURN SAMSON OVER TO THEM, THE TRIBAL LEADERS AGREE. "IT'S YOU," THEY TELL SAMSON, "OR EVERY MAN, WOMAN AND CHILD IN JUDAH." SO SAMSON SURRENDERS...

THAT OUGHT TO DO IT. THE ROPES ARE NEW, AND THE KNOTS ARE TIGHT. HE'S HELPLESS-- LET'S GO.

O GOD, BE WITH ME WHEN I FACE MY ENEMY.

IT'S A GREAT MOMENT FOR THE PHILISTINES WHEN SAMSON IS BOUND AND DELIVERED INTO THEIR HANDS.

WONDER HOW THE STRONG MAN FEELS NOW?

I'D LIKE TO BE THE FIRST ONE TO GET EVEN WITH HIM.

NOT I-- I DON'T TRUST ROPES TO HOLD SAMSON.

WAIT TILL WE SHOW THE MIGHTY MAN OF JUDAH TO THE PEOPLE BACK HOME.

THAT JAWBONE-- IT'S JUST WHAT I NEED!

The Big Bribe

FROM JUDGES 16: 3-5

WHEN THE PHILISTINES LEARN THAT SAMSON IS IN THEIR CITY THEY CALL OUT ALL THE GUARDS AND LIE IN WAIT FOR HIM.

I'VE NEVER SEEN SAMSON. WHAT'S HE LIKE?

LIKE ANYBODY ELSE--EXCEPT THAT HIS HAIR IS LONG AND HIS STRENGTH IS GREATER THAN A HUNDRED MEN.

AT MIDNIGHT SAMSON WALKS DOWN THE STREET AND TOWARD THE GATE...

HMM--HEAVY GUARD ON DUTY TONIGHT. CAN'T BE THAT THEY WANT TO HELP ME THROUGH THE GATE, SO...

I'LL HELP MYSELF!

STOP HIM! DON'T LET HIM GET AWAY!

Blind Captive

FROM JUDGES 16: 6-21

FOR 5500 PIECES OF SILVER DELILAH HAS PROMISED TO FIND OUT THE SOURCE OF SAMSON'S STRENGTH AND REPORT IT TO HIS PHILISTINE ENEMIES. SO SHE PRETENDS SHE LOVES HIM...

YOU'RE SO STRONG, SAMSON... ARE THERE NO BONDS THAT CAN HOLD YOU?

IF I WERE TIED WITH SEVEN NEW BOWSTRINGS, I'D BE NO STRONGER THAN ANY OTHER MAN.

ON SAMSON'S NEXT VISIT, HE FALLS ASLEEP AND DELILAH TIES HIM WITH SEVEN NEW BOWSTRINGS.

THIS WILL HOLD HIM! SOON THE REWARD WILL BE MINE!

WAKE UP, SAMSON! THE PHILISTINES ARE HERE!

219

WATCH OUT--HE'S FREE! RUN FOR YOUR LIVES!

SAMSON TRICKED ME!

DELILAH KEEPS TRYING TO LEARN THE SECRET OF SAMSON'S STRENGTH. SHE BINDS HIM IN DIFFERENT WAYS, BUT EACH TIME HE BREAKS FREE. AT LAST...

YOU DON'T LOVE ME, SAMSON! IF YOU DID, YOU'D TELL ME THE TRUTH.

I DO LOVE YOU, AND TO PROVE IT, I'LL TELL YOU MY SECRET. WHEN I WAS DEDICATED TO GOD A PROMISE WAS MADE NEVER TO CUT MY HAIR. IF I BREAK THAT PROMISE, GOD WILL TAKE AWAY MY STRENGTH. I'LL BE AS WEAK AS ANY MAN.

AT LAST DELILAH HAS THE REAL SECRET. SHE CALLS THE PHILISTINES AND PLANS TO TRAP SAMSON THAT NIGHT.

HAVE YOUR CHAINS READY-- AND TELL YOUR MASTERS TO BRING THE MONEY THEY PROMISED ME.

THAT EVENING SAMSON CALLS ON DELILAH. WHEN HE FALLS ASLEEP...

NOW'S YOUR CHANCE.

I'VE NEVER SEEN SUCH LONG HAIR-- BUT I STILL DON'T SEE HOW THIS WILL TAKE HIS STRENGTH AWAY.

SAMSON! WAKE UP-- THE PHILISTINES ARE HERE.

Samson's Victory

FROM JUDGES 16: 21-30

BETRAYED BY DELILAH, SAMSON IS CAPTURED BY THE PHILISTINES, BLINDED, AND MADE TO GRIND GRAIN IN THE PRISON AT GAZA. BUT—UNNOTICED BY HIS CAPTORS—HIS HAIR BEGINS TO GROW...

O GOD, GIVE ME ONE MORE CHANCE TO FREE MY PEOPLE FROM THE SLAVERY OF THE PHILISTINES!

OUTSIDE THE PRISON WALLS, THE PHILISTINES PREPARE FOR A GREAT FESTIVAL TO DAGON, THEIR GOD.

BRING YOUR GIFTS TO DAGON WHO DELIVERED SAMSON INTO OUR HANDS.

DURING THE FEAST...

WHAT CAN WE DO TO PLEASE THE CROWD?

I HAVE IT—BRING SAMSON OUT AND LET THE PEOPLE HAVE THEIR FUN WITH HIM.

222

SO SAMSON IS BROUGHT OUT OF PRISON AND LED UP THE TEMPLE STEPS...

BRING HIM UP HERE SO EVERYONE CAN SEE WHAT THE MIGHTY JUDGE OF ISRAEL LOOKS LIKE NOW!

SHOW US HOW YOU CARRIED OFF THE GATES OF GAZA!

LET'S SEE YOU TEAR A LION APART WITH YOUR HANDS.

AS SAMSON'S HAIR HAS GROWN— SO HAS HIS STRENGTH...

WHERE ARE THE PILLARS? I WANT TO LEAN AGAINST THEM.

HERE— I'LL PUT YOUR HANDS ON THEM.

RUN, BOY—AND DON'T STOP UNTIL YOU'RE OUTSIDE THE TEMPLE.

USING ALL HIS MIGHTY STRENGTH, SAMSON PUSHES AGAINST THE PILLARS—AND THE GIANT TEMPLE TO THE HEATHEN GOD, DAGON, CRASHES TO THE GROUND. CRUSHED BENEATH IT ARE THE PHILISTINES WHO HAD MADE SLAVES OF SAMSON'S PEOPLE...

BUT THE FIGHT IS NOT YET OVER...AND IN THE MIDST OF THESE TROUBLESOME TIMES THERE COMES A WOMAN FROM A FOREIGN LAND WHO GIVES ISRAEL A VICTORIOUS KING.

Naomi's Strategy

FROM RUTH 2: 6—3: 18

THE GLEANERS WATCH EAGERLY AS BOAZ, THE OWNER OF THE FIELDS, QUESTIONS HIS FOREMAN ABOUT THE YOUNG WOMAN GATHERING GRAIN IN HIS FIELDS.

HER NAME IS RUTH—SHE IS THE MOABITE WOMAN WHO TAKES CARE OF HER MOTHER-IN-LAW, NAOMI.

HOW BEAUTIFUL SHE IS!

I HAVE HEARD HOW KIND YOU ARE TO YOUR MOTHER-IN-LAW. GLEAN IN MY FIELDS AS MUCH AS YOU LIKE —AND MAY GOD REWARD AND PROTECT YOU.

THANK YOU. YOU ARE VERY KIND.

AT LUNCH TIME BOAZ INVITES RUTH TO EAT WITH HIM AND HIS REAPERS.

AND WHEN THE MEAL IS OVER AND RUTH HAS GONE BACK TO WORK—

DROP SOME GRAIN ON PURPOSE FOR HER TO PICK UP, AND SEE THAT NO HARM COMES TO HER!

HAVE NO FEAR, BOAZ. SHE WILL BE SAFE—AND SHE WILL FIND ALL THE GRAIN SHE NEEDS.

THAT EVENING—

LOOK AT ALL THE GRAIN I FOUND! OH, NAOMI, YOUR GOD IS GOOD TO US.

I THOUGHT WHEN MY HUSBAND AND SONS DIED THAT GOD HAD FORGOTTEN ME. NOW I KNOW HOW MUCH HE LOVES ME, FOR HE HAS GIVEN ME A DAUGHTER-IN-LAW WHO CARES FOR ME AS A DAUGHTER. BUT—NOW—TELL ME ABOUT THE DAY. IN WHOSE FIELD DID YOU GLEAN?

HIS NAME WAS BOAZ—HE WAS VERY KIND.

AND VERY HANDSOME, TOO.

BOAZ? HE IS A RELATIVE OF MY HUSBAND'S FAMILY. GOD BLESS HIM FOR BEING KIND TO YOU.

ALL THROUGH THE HARVEST SEASON RUTH GLEANS IN BOAZ' FIELD AND TAKES CARE OF NAOMI. ONE EVENING...

I BELIEVE BOAZ LOVES YOU, BUT HE DOESN'T KNOW HOW YOU FEEL. WE ISRAELITES HAVE A CUSTOM ABOUT THE RIGHTS OF RELATIVES IN MARRIAGE. TONIGHT BOAZ WILL STAY AT THE THRESHING FLOOR TO GUARD HIS GRAIN. IF YOU DO AS I SAY—

I LOVE BOAZ, AND I'LL DO WHAT YOU TELL ME.

227

Ancestress of a King

FROM RUTH 4

NEXT MORNING BOAZ WATCHES FOR THE RELATIVE WHO HAS FIRST RIGHT TO BUY THE LAND THAT BELONGED TO NAOMI'S DEAD HUSBAND—AND TO MARRY RUTH.

GOOD MORNING! WILL YOU STOP AND DISCUSS A MATTER THAT IS IMPORTANT TO BOTH OF US?

GOOD MORNING TO YOU, BOAZ. WHAT IS THE PROBLEM?

WHEN THE MAN IS SEATED BOAZ INVITES THE ELDERS OF THE CITY TO JOIN THEM...

THE LAND THAT BELONGED TO NAOMI'S HUSBAND IS FOR SALE. ONE OF US MUST BUY IT TO KEEP IT IN THE FAMILY. YOU ARE THE CLOSEST RELATIVE... WILL YOU BUY THE LAND?

YES, I WILL BUY IT!

THE NEWS OF RUTH AND BOAZ' COMING MARRIAGE SPREADS RAPIDLY THROUGHOUT ALL BETHLEHEM, FOR BOAZ IS A WELL-TO-DO LANDOWNER. AT THE WEDDING THERE IS FEASTING, MUSIC AND LAUGHTER...

ARE YOU HAPPY, MY DEAR?

HAPPIER THAN I EVER DREAMED I COULD BE. GOD HAS BEEN GOOD TO ME.

AFTER HER MARRIAGE, RUTH MOVES INTO THE BIG HOUSE OF BOAZ. LATER, WHEN A SON IS BORN TO RUTH, NAOMI PROUDLY CARES FOR THE CHILD. HE IS NAMED OBED, WHICH MEANS "SERVANT."

OH, RUTH, I THANK GOD FOR THE DAY YOU LEFT MOAB TO COME WITH ME TO BETHLEHEM. FOR NOW I HAVE A GRANDSON TO SERVE ME IN MY OLD AGE.

I THANK HIM, TOO, NAOMI — FOR TRULY YOUR PEOPLE HAVE BECOME MY PEOPLE — AND YOUR GOD MY GOD...

AND MY PRAYER IS THAT OBED WILL SERVE GOD AND HIS PEOPLE.

RUTH'S PRAYER COMES TRUE — FOR HER SON BECOMES THE GRANDFATHER OF DAVID, ISRAEL'S GREATEST KING, WHO FREES HIS PEOPLE FROM THEIR ENEMIES...

Call in the Night

FROM I SAMUEL 1: 1—3: 17

HUNDREDS OF YEARS HAVE PASSED SINCE THE ISRAELITES SETTLED IN THE PROMISED LAND OF CANAAN. DURING THAT TIME THEY OFTEN TURNED FROM GOD TO WORSHIP HEATHEN IDOLS. AS A RESULT THEY HAVE BECOME WEAK— ALMOST SLAVES OF THEIR ENEMIES, THE PHILISTINES. TO SOME IT SEEMS THAT GOD HAS FORGOTTEN HIS PROMISE TO MAKE ISRAEL STRONG.

THE BOOK OF **1 SAMUEL** BEGINS...

AT THE TABERNACLE AT SHILOH, ELI, THE HIGH PRIEST, WATCHES THE FAITHFUL COME TO WORSHIP. HE NOTICES A WOMAN AND SUDDENLY HE BECOMES ANGRY...

SHE ACTS AS IF SHE'S DRUNK! HOW DARE SHE INSULT GOD!

ANGRILY HE ACCUSES HER...

NO! NO! I AM NOT DRUNK, I AM UNHAPPY; AND IN MY SORROW I HAVE POURED OUT MY HEART TO GOD, ASKING HIM TO HELP ME.

GO IN PEACE, HANNAH, AND MAY GOD GRANT THEE THY PRAYER.

HANNAH IS SO HAPPY THAT SHE RUSHES OUT OF THE TABERNACLE TO FIND HER HUSBAND.

OH, ELKANAH, I PRAYED TO GOD FOR A SON—AND ELI BLESSED ME AND ASKED GOD TO GIVE ME WHAT I PRAYED FOR.

A SON? I, TOO, PRAY THAT GOD WILL GRANT YOUR PRAYER.

GOD ANSWERS HANNAH'S PRAYER—AND WHEN THE BOY IS OLD ENOUGH TO LEAVE HIS MOTHER, SHE BRINGS HIM TO ELI.

WHEN I ASKED GOD FOR A SON, I PROMISED THAT HE WOULD SERVE THE LORD ALL HIS LIFE. SO I HAVE BROUGHT HIM HERE TO BE TRAINED IN GOD'S HOUSE. HIS NAME IS SAMUEL.

GOD BLESS YOU, HANNAH. LEAVE THE BOY WITH ME AND I WILL TEACH HIM TO BE A SERVANT OF THE LORD.

SAMUEL STAYS WITH ELI AND EAGERLY LEARNS WHAT GOD EXPECTS OF THOSE WHO SERVE HIM. EACH YEAR WHEN HANNAH AND HER HUSBAND COME TO WORSHIP, SHE BRINGS SAMUEL A NEW COAT.

IT'S JUST LIKE A PRIEST'S ROBE. THANK YOU, MOTHER.

OLD ELI IS PROUD OF SAMUEL—BUT HE IS BROKENHEARTED WHEN HE THINKS OF HIS OWN TWO SONS. AS PRIESTS, THEY HAVE SINNED AGAINST GOD AND CHEATED THE PEOPLE. ELI KNOWS THAT HE, TOO, IS GUILTY BECAUSE HE HAS DONE NOTHING TO STOP THEM.

In a Heathen Temple

FROM 1 SAMUEL 3: 18—5: 2

ELI, THE HIGH PRIEST OF ISRAEL, KNOWS THAT GOD HAS SPOKEN TO HIS YOUNG HELPER, SAMUEL. SAMUEL DOESN'T WANT TO REPEAT THE MESSAGE, BUT ELI INSISTS...

GOD SAID, "ELI'S SONS ARE WICKED AND ELI HAS NOT TRIED TO STOP THEM. THEY WILL BE PUNISHED FOR THE EVIL THEY HAVE DONE."

THE LORD WILL DO WHAT IS JUST.

WORD SPREADS THAT GOD HAS SPOKEN TO SAMUEL. AND AS SAMUEL GROWS UP ALL ISRAEL KNOWS THAT HE IS A TRUE PROPHET OF GOD.

IF ONLY OUR PRIESTS WERE MEN OF GOD LIKE SAMUEL. HOW LONG MUST WE SUFFER UNDER THE LYING AND CHEATING OF ELI'S SONS?

MARK MY WORDS, THEY WILL BRING ABOUT THEIR OWN DESTRUCTION.

SUDDENLY WAR BREAKS OUT WITH THE PHILISTINES. A FIERCE BATTLE RAGES, AND THE ISRAELITES ARE BADLY DEFEATED.

WE'VE LOST FOUR THOUSAND MEN.

WHAT CAN WE DO?

The Turning Point

FROM 1 SAMUEL 5: 3—7: 10

WITH SHOUTS OF TRIUMPH THE PHILISTINES PLACE THE SACRED ARK OF GOD IN THEIR HEATHEN TEMPLE. TO THEM IT IS A SIGN THAT THE PHILISTINE GOD, DAGON, HAS CONQUERED THE GOD OF ISRAEL. BUT THE NEXT MORNING THE IDOL LIES ON ITS FACE BEFORE THE ARK. PRIESTS REPLACE THE IDOL, AND ON THE FOLLOWING MORNING...

LOOK! OUR GREAT GOD, DAGON, LIES BROKEN BEFORE THE ARK OF THE ISRAELITES!

SO THE ARK IS TAKEN FROM ONE PHILISTINE CITY TO ANOTHER...AND IN EACH CITY A PLAGUE BREAKS OUT...

NOT A FAMILY HAS ESCAPED THIS STRANGE ILLNESS.

OUR FIELDS ARE OVER RUN WITH MICE. I TELL YOU—A CURSE HAS BEEN PUT UPON THIS CITY.

THE PHILISTINES SOON REALIZE THAT THEIR TROUBLES BEGAN WHEN THEY CAPTURED THE HOLY ARK OF ISRAEL. FINALLY THEY RETURN THE ARK TO ISRAEL, BUT ISRAEL IS WORSHIPING IDOLS. THE ARK IS PLACED IN A HOUSE AND ALMOST FORGOTTEN.

BUT AFTER YEARS OF STRUGGLE UNDER THE PHILISTINES, THE ISRAELITES ARE READY TO LISTEN WHEN SAMUEL SPEAKS...

RETURN TO THE LORD! WORSHIP HIM WITH ALL YOUR HEARTS, AND GOD WILL DELIVER YOU FROM THE PHILISTINES.

SAMUEL IS RIGHT! LET US THROW AWAY OUR IDOLS AND WORSHIP GOD.

LET US ALL GO TO THE CITY OF MIZPEH AND PRAY TOGETHER!

EAGERLY THE PEOPLE FOLLOW THIS MAN WHO SPEAKS BOLDLY FOR GOD. BY THE THOUSANDS THEY SET OUT...

BUT THE GREAT MARCH TO MIZPEH IS DISCOVERED BY THE PHILISTINES.

IF THOUSANDS OF ISRAELITES ARE MASSING AT MIZPEH IT CAN MEAN ONLY ONE THING — THEY PLAN TO ATTACK US.

LET'S STRIKE BEFORE THEY DO, AND **THIS** TIME WE'LL CRUSH THEM SO BADLY THEY'LL NEVER FIGHT AGAIN!

238

A Prophet Speaks

FROM I SAMUEL 7: 10—9: 20

239

GOD HAS ANSWERED OUR PRAYER.

LET'S GO AFTER THEM.

THE PHILISTINE DEFEAT IS A TURNING POINT IN ISRAEL'S HISTORY—NEVER AGAIN DO THE PHILISTINES INVADE ISRAEL WHILE SAMUEL IS ITS LEADER. TO REMIND HIS PEOPLE THAT IT WAS GOD WHO HELPED THEM WIN THEIR VICTORY, SAMUEL ERECTS A STONE WHICH HE CALLS EBENEZER (STONE OF HELP).

FOR YEARS SAMUEL JUDGES THE PEOPLE OF ISRAEL, AND THERE IS PEACE. BUT AS HE GROWS OLD THE TRIBAL LEADERS BECOME WORRIED...

SAMUEL, YOU ARE GROWING OLD, AND YOUR SONS ARE NOT WORTHY TO TAKE YOUR PLACE AS JUDGE OF ISRAEL. GIVE US A KING LIKE OTHER NATIONS HAVE.

I WILL PRAY TO GOD ABOUT YOUR REQUEST.

LATER—

THE LORD HAS TOLD ME TO WARN YOU WHAT A KING WILL DO—HE WILL SEND YOUR SONS TO BATTLE, YOUR DAUGHTERS WILL BECOME HIS SERVANTS, AND YOUR BEST CROPS WILL BE USED TO FEED HIS COURT.

MAYBE SO, BUT WE STILL WANT A KING!

AGAIN SAMUEL PRAYS TO GOD, THEN—

GOD WANTS ME TO DO AS YOU HAVE ASKED. GO HOME, AND I WILL SEND WORD WHEN I HAVE FOUND A KING FOR YOU.

A FEW DAYS LATER SAMUEL SETS OUT EAGERLY FOR THE GATE OF THE CITY—

YESTERDAY GOD TOLD ME THAT TODAY I WOULD MEET A MAN, HERE, WHO IS THE ONE TO BE THE KING OF ISRAEL.

AT THE GATE, A YOUNG FARMER WHO IS LOOKING FOR HIS LOST DONKEYS STOPS SAMUEL.

I NEED HELP. CAN YOU TELL ME WHERE I MIGHT FIND THE PROPHET, SAMUEL?

I AM THE PROPHET. DON'T WORRY ABOUT YOUR DONKEYS —THEY HAVE BEEN FOUND. COME WITH ME TO WORSHIP THE LORD, AND TOMORROW I WILL TELL YOU WHAT GREAT THINGS ARE IN STORE FOR YOU.

GREAT THINGS— FOR ME? WHAT DOES HE MEAN?

Test for a King

FROM 1 SAMUEL 9: 20—11: 7

THE YOUNG FARMER, SAUL, IS STUNNED WHEN SAMUEL TELLS HIM THAT GREAT THINGS ARE IN STORE FOR HIM. THEY WORSHIP GOD TOGETHER, THEN SAMUEL INVITES SAUL TO A SPECIAL FEAST.

WHY SHOULD THIS YOUNG MAN BE SO HIGHLY HONORED?

SAMUEL MAKES NO EXPLANATION TO HIS GUESTS, BUT EARLY THE NEXT MORNING HE ACCOMPANIES SAUL AND HIS SERVANT AS THEY LEAVE THE CITY.

SEND YOUR SERVANT ON AHEAD, SAUL. I HAVE A MESSAGE FOR YOU FROM GOD.

THE LORD HAS ANOINTED YOU TO RULE OVER HIS PEOPLE. CALL ON THE LORD, AND HE WILL BE WITH YOU.

SURPRISED—AND A LITTLE FRIGHTENED—AT ALL THAT HAS HAPPENED TO HIM, SAUL STARTS HOME. BUT ON THE WAY THE SPIRIT OF GOD COMES TO HIM. HOWEVER, WHEN HE REACHES HOME, HE DOES NOT TELL ANYONE THAT HE HAS BEEN ANOINTED KING!

WHEN SAMUEL CALLS THE PEOPLE TO MIZPEH, SAUL GOES, TOO. BEFORE ALL ISRAEL SAMUEL MAKES A SURPRISING ANNOUNCEMENT.

GOD HAS CHOSEN SAUL TO RULE OVER YOU.

WHERE **IS** HE?

A SEARCH IS QUICKLY MADE, AND SAUL—WHO IS AWED BY THE THOUGHT OF BEING KING—IS FOUND HIDING.

WHEN HE IS BROUGHT FORTH, THE PEOPLE SHOUT: LONG LIVE THE KING!

AT MIZPEH THE PEOPLE SHOUTED THEIR PRAISES TO SAUL—BUT AFTER HE RETURNS HOME, SOME COMPLAIN.

FINE THING—THERE GOES OUR KING—BACK TO THE FARM.

HE'LL BE NO HELP TO US.

SAUL'S TEST AS A LEADER COMES WHEN HE RETURNS HOME FROM HIS FIELDS ONE DAY AND FINDS THE WHOLE VILLAGE WEEPING.

WHAT'S THE MATTER?

HAVEN'T YOU HEARD? THE AMMONITES HAVE SURROUNDED JABESH. THEY THREATEN TO PUT OUT AN EYE OF EVERY MAN IN THE CITY.

WE'LL SHOW THE AMMONITES THEY CAN'T THREATEN ISRAEL!

IT'S NO USE. YOU'LL NEVER GET ENOUGH PEOPLE TO HELP YOU FIGHT THE AMMONITES.

I'M KING—AND I'LL **MAKE** THEM FIGHT!

BIG TALK—BUT WAIT UNTIL HE TRIES TO BACK IT UP.

By Order of the King

FROM 1 SAMUEL 11—13: 9

WHEN WORD COMES THAT THE AMMONITES HAVE SURROUNDED AN ISRAELITE CITY, SAUL FACES HIS FIRST TEST AS KING. TO HIS AMAZEMENT—AND ANGER—HE DISCOVERS THAT SOME OF HIS PEOPLE ARE AFRAID TO FIGHT! HE ACTS AT ONCE...

BY ORDER OF THE KING WE ARE TO KILL THE OXEN OF ANY MAN WHO REFUSES TO DEFEND HIS COUNTRY!

ER—I'LL JOIN THE ARMY RIGHT NOW!

AN ARMY IS QUICKLY FORMED, AND SAUL ATTACKS AT DAWN. CAUGHT BY SURPRISE, THE AMMONITES ARE DEFEATED.

PROUD OF THEIR VICTORY, THE ISRAELITES SHOUT THEIR PRAISES TO SAUL.

SURE, THEY'RE **ALL** FOR YOU TODAY. BUT WHAT ABOUT THE MEN WHO DIDN'T WANT YOU TO BE KING? THEY SHOULD BE KILLED.

NO! NO MAN SHALL BE PUT TO DEATH FOR THAT.

NOW THAT ISRAEL HAS A KING, SAMUEL PREPARES TO WITHDRAW FROM HIS POSITION AS JUDGE OF ISRAEL. BUT BEFORE HE DOES, HE CALLS THE PEOPLE TOGETHER AND SPEAKS TO THEM AS THE PROPHET OF GOD.

OBEY THE LORD AND SERVE YOUR KING, AND ALL WILL BE WELL WITH YOU. BUT IF YOU RETURN TO ANY OF YOUR WICKED WAYS, YOU SHALL BE DESTROYED — BOTH YOU AND YOUR KING!

SPURRED ON BY HIS VICTORY OVER THE AMMONITES, SAUL FORMS A STANDING ARMY AND PREPARES TO WIN HIS PEOPLE'S FREEDOM FROM THE PHILISTINES. HIS SON, JONATHAN, MAKES A SUCCESSFUL ATTACK ON A PHILISTINE GARRISON—AND AGAIN ISRAEL CHEERS.

BUT WHEN WORD REACHES THE MAIN ARMY OF THE PHILISTINES...

TAKE THIRTY THOUSAND CHARIOTS, SIX THOUSAND HORSEMEN AND ALL OUR INFANTRY—SET UP A CAMP AT MICHMASH. FROM THERE WE CAN SEND OUT RAIDING PARTIES THAT WILL DRAW SAUL FROM HIS STRONGHOLD AT GILGAL.

IN SPITE OF FORMER VICTORIES MANY OF THE ISRAELITES LOSE COURAGE WHEN THEY SEE THE SIZE OF THE ENEMY FORCES.

THE PHILISTINES OUTNUMBER US BY THOUSANDS. I'M HIDING OUT UNTIL THIS IS OVER.

THERE'S A PIT DOWN THE VALLEY— I'LL HIDE THERE.

EVEN IN THE CAMP OF KING SAUL, THE SOLDIERS ARE AFRAID.

A RAID ON A PHILISTINE GARRISON IS ONE THING—FIGHTING THE WHOLE PHILISTINE ARMY IS ANOTHER.

THE MEN ARE LOSING THEIR NERVE. WE CAN'T WAIT MUCH LONGER FOR SAMUEL TO COME AND OFFER THE SACRIFICE TO GOD.

YOU'RE RIGHT. WE'LL WAIT NO LONGER. I'LL MAKE THE OFFERING!

The King Disobeys

FROM 1 SAMUEL 13: 10—15: 14

THE ISRAELITES WATCH WITH GROWING TERROR AS THE PHILISTINE ARMY SETS UP CAMP AT MICHMASH. SAUL, AFRAID THAT HIS PEOPLE WILL PANIC, LOSES FAITH IN GOD'S GUIDANCE. INSTEAD OF WAITING FOR SAMUEL TO OFFER THE SACRIFICE, HE MAKES THE OFFERING HIMSELF. HE NO SOONER FINISHES THAN HE SEES SAMUEL COMING...

I WAS AFRAID MY PEOPLE WOULD FLEE BEFORE YOU GOT HERE, SO I OFFERED THE SACRIFICE.

YOU HAVE DISOBEYED GOD. YOU CANNOT DO THAT AND HOLD YOUR KINGDOM!

MEANTIME—INSTEAD OF MAKING AN OPEN ATTACK, THE PHILISTINES SEND OUT RAIDING PARTIES TO DRAW SAUL FROM CAMP—BUT SAUL WILL NOT COME OUT. HIS SON, PRINCE JONATHAN, DECIDES TO TAKE ACTION...

LET'S ATTACK THE PHILISTINE GARRISON BY OURSELVES.

I'M WITH YOU!

SECRETLY JONATHAN AND HIS ARMOR-BEARER LEAVE CAMP. WHEN THEY REACH THE FOOT OF THE CLIFF THAT LEADS TO THE PHILISTINE GARRISON, THE ENEMY DARES THEM TO COME UP AND FIGHT. BOLDLY, JONATHAN AND HIS FRIEND SCALE THE CLIFF...

FOLLOW ME, FOR WITH THE LORD THERE IS NO NEED FOR LARGE NUMBERS.

AT THE TOP THEY ATTACK WITH SUCH DARING THAT THE PHILISTINES FLEE IN PANIC. IN THEIR CONFUSION, THE PHILISTINES EVEN ATTACK ONE ANOTHER.

WHEN SAUL LEARNS THE PHILISTINES ARE RETREATING, AND DISCOVERS THAT IT IS JONATHAN WHO HAS ATTACKED THEM, HE LEADS HIS ARMY AGAINST THE ENEMY AND DRIVES THEM BACK TO THEIR OWN COUNTRY.

AFTER THIS VICTORY, SAUL ATTACKS THE OTHER ENEMIES OF ISRAEL AND DRIVES THEM AWAY. BUT THE RAIDS OF THE DESERT TRIBE OF THE AMALEKITES CONTINUE —

FINALLY SAMUEL CALLS SAUL TO HIM...

THE LORD WANTS YOU TO DESTROY THE AMALEKITES WHO HAVE BEEN ENEMIES OF ISRAEL EVER SINCE OUR PEOPLE LEFT EGYPT. BRING NOTHING AWAY WITH YOU, FOR THIS IS NOT A WAR TO GAIN WEALTH.

SAUL ATTACKS THE AMALEKITES AND DRIVES THEM BACK TOWARD EGYPT, BUT HE BRINGS THE BEST OF THE SHEEP AND OXEN HOME WITH HIM.

AT GILGAL, HE COMES FACE TO FACE WITH SAMUEL...

I HAVE OBEYED THE COMMANDMENT OF GOD AND DESTROYED THE AMALEKITES.

IF YOU HAVE OBEYED GOD, THEN WHAT IS THE MEANING OF THIS NOISE OF SHEEP AND CATTLE THAT I HEAR?

A Mysterious Visit

FROM 1 Samuel 15: 15—16: 11

SEVEN OF JESSE'S SONS APPEAR BEFORE SAMUEL— BUT NOT ONE OF THEM IS CHOSEN.

HAVE I SEEN ALL OF YOUR SONS?

NO, THE YOUNGEST, DAVID, IS TENDING THE SHEEP. I'LL SEND ONE OF MY SONS AND A SERVANT FOR HIM.

WONDER WHY SAMUEL INSISTS UPON SEEING DAVID?

THE WHOLE THING IS A MYSTERY.

JESSE'S SON FINDS HIS BROTHER IN THE FIELDS OUTSIDE BETHLEHEM.

THERE'S DAVID.

LOOK—A LION— AND DAVID DOESN'T SEE IT!

The Chosen One

FROM I SAMUEL 16: 12-19

WHEN SAMUEL, THE PROPHET OF GOD, ASKS TO SEE ALL OF JESSE'S SONS, JESSE HAS TO SEND FOR HIS YOUNGEST, DAVID, WHO IS AWAY TENDING SHEEP. THE MESSENGERS REACH THE FIELDS IN TIME TO SEE A LION ABOUT TO SPRING ON THE YOUNG SHEPHERD. DAVID'S KEEN EARS HEAR A SWISH IN THE TALL GRASS. HE WHIRLS...

A LION!

DAVID! THE LION—YOU KILLED IT!

I KILLED A BEAR A FEW DAYS AGO. NOTHING'S GOING TO HURT MY FATHER'S SHEEP IF I CAN HELP IT.

YOU'RE A BRAVE SHEPHERD, DAVID. BUT HURRY HOME—SAMUEL WANTS TO SEE YOU. I'VE BROUGHT A MAN TO STAY WITH THE SHEEP.

ME? BUT WHY?

ON THE HIKE BACK TO THE CITY, DAVID CONTINUES TO WONDER. BUT WHEN SAMUEL SEES THE YOUNG SHEPHERD BOY, HE KNOWS HIS SEARCH HAS ENDED, FOR HE HEARS GOD SAY: *"THIS IS MY CHOSEN ONE."*

BEFORE JESSE AND HIS SONS, SAMUEL BLESSES DAVID AND ANOINTS HIS HEAD WITH OIL.

THE LORD BLESS YOU, FOR YOU WILL BE THE NEXT KING OF ISRAEL.

DAVID DOES NOT KNOW WHEN HE WILL BE MADE KING. BUT AS HE GOES BACK TO HIS SHEEP HE HAS A SPECIAL FEELING OF GOD'S PRESENCE WITH HIM.

THE LORD IS MY STRENGTH. WHAT HAVE I TO FEAR?